J
COL   Collections for young
         scholars, Vol 4 Book 1

DATE DUE

JUL 13 2000		
AUG 02 2000		
AUG 02 2000		
OCT 06 2000		

GAYLORD   #3523PI   Printed in USA

COLLECTIONS
FOR YOUNG SCHOLARS™

VOLUME 4 BOOK I

Risks and Consequences

Business

Medicine

Art by Yoriko Ito

COLLECTIONS FOR YOUNG SCHOLARS™

VOLUME 4 BOOK I

PROGRAM AUTHORS
Carl Bereiter
Ann Brown
Marlene Scardamalia
Valerie Anderson
Joe Campione

CONSULTING AUTHORS
Michael Pressley
Iva Carruthers
Bill Pinkney

OPEN COURT PUBLISHING COMPANY
CHICAGO AND PERU, ILLINOIS

CHAIRMAN
M. Blouke Carus

PRESIDENT
André W. Carus

EDUCATION DIRECTOR
Carl Bereiter

CONCEPT
Barbara Conteh

EXECUTIVE EDITOR
Shirley Graudin

MANAGING EDITOR
Sheelagh McGurn

PROJECT EDITOR
Wiley Blevins

ART DIRECTOR
John Grandits

VICE-PRESIDENT, PRODUCTION
AND MANUFACTURING
Chris Vancalbergh

PERMISSIONS COORDINATOR
Diane Sikora

COVER ARTIST
Yoriko Ito

Printed in the United States of America

ISBN 0-8126-4148-5

10 9 8 7 6 5 4

ACKNOWLEDGMENTS

Grateful acknowledgment is given to the following publishers and copyright owners for permission granted to reprint selections from their publications. All possible care has been taken to trace ownership and secure permission for each selection included.

Abingdon Press: "Sewed Up His Heart" adapted from *Sure Hands, Strong Heart: The Life of Daniel Hale Williams* by Lillie Patterson, copyright © 1981 by Abingdon.

Atheneum Publishers, an imprint of Macmillan Publishing Co.: An excerpt entitled "Mrs. Frisby and the Crow" from *Mrs. Frisby and the Rats of NIMH* by Robert C. O'Brien, copyright © 1971 by Robert C. O'Brien. An excerpt from *Eddie, Incorporated* by Phyllis Reynolds Naylor, text copyright © 1980 by Phyllis Reynolds Naylor. An excerpt from *Shadow of a Bull* by Maia Wojciechowska, copyright © 1964 by Maia Wojciechowska.

Peter Bedrick Books: An excerpt from *Two Tickets to Freedom* by Florence B. Freedman, text copyright © 1971 by Florence B. Freedman.

Curtis Brown, Ltd.: "The Microscope" by Maxine Kumin from *The Wonderful Babies of 1809 (and Other Years)*, text copyright © 1963 by Maxine W. Kumin, first published in the *Atlantic Monthly*.

Marion Marsh Brown: An excerpt entitled "The Story of Susan La Flesche Picotte" from *Homeward the Arrow's Flight* by Marion Marsh Brown, copyright © 1980 by Marion Marsh Brown.

Carolrhoda Books, Inc., Minneapolis, MN: "Birth of a Baby Food" from *The Problem Solvers: People Who Turned Problems into Products* by Nathan Aaseng, copyright © 1989 by Lerner Publications Co. *The Bridge Dancers* by Carol Saller, illustrated by Gerald Talifero, text copyright © 1990 by the author, illustrations © 1991 by Carolrhoda Books, Inc.

Dutton Children's Books, a division of Penguin USA Inc.,: *The King's Fountain* by Lloyd Alexander, illustrated by Ezra Jack Keats, text copyright © 1971 by Lloyd Alexander, illustrations copyright © 1971 by Ezra Jack Keats.

Facts on File, Inc., New York: An excerpt entitled "Amelia Earhart, Fly On" from *Amelia Earhart* by Carol Ann Pearce, copyright © 1988 by Carol Ann Pearce.

Farrar, Straus & Giroux, Inc.: *Salt*, retold by Harve Zemach, illustrated by Margot Zemach, copyright © 1965 by Margot Zemach.

Harcourt Brace & Co.: "People Who Must" from *Early Moon* by Carl Sandburg, copyright 1930 by Harcourt Brace & Co., copyright © renewed 1958 by Carl Sandburg.

HarperCollins Publishers: An excerpt from *Sarah, Plain and Tall* by Patricia MacLachlan, copyright © 1985 by Patricia MacLachlan. *The Girl Who Loved the Wind* by Jane Yolen, illustrated by Ed Young, copyright © 1972 by Berne Convention. "Tin-Peddler" from *Farmer Boy* by Laura Ingalls Wilder, illustrated by Garth Williams, text copyright 1933 by Laura Ingalls Wilder, copyright © renewed 1961 by Roger L. MacBride, illustrations copyright 1953 by Garth Williams.

Henry Holt and Co., Inc.: An excerpt from *Business Is Looking Up* by Barbara Aiello and Jeffrey Shulman, copyright © 1988 by The Kids on the Block, Inc.

Little, Brown and Co.: "The Germ" from *Verses from 1929 On* by Ogden Nash, copyright 1933 by Ogden Nash. "Surgeons Must Be Very Careful" from *The Poems of Emily Dickinson*, edited by Martha Dickinson Bianchi and Alfred Leete Hampson.

John Loeper: "Fireman's Song, 1845" from *By Hook and Ladder: The Story of Fire Fighting in America* by John J. Loeper, copyright © 1981 by John J. Loeper.

Mary Malone: An excerpt from *Andrew Carnegie: Giant of Industry* by Mary Malone, copyright © 1969 by Mary Malone.

Carol Mann Agency and Coward, McCann and Geoghegan: *Toto* by Marietta Moskin, illustrated by Rocco Negri, text copyright © 1971 by Marietta Moskin, illustrations copyright © 1971 by Rocco Negri.

Margaret K. McElderry Books, an imprint of Macmillan Publishing Co.: "Lemonade Stand" from *Worlds I Know and Other Poems* by Myra Cohn Livingston, copyright © 1985 by Myra Cohn Livingston.

continued on page 320

 5

RISKS AND CONSEQUENCES

❧

BUSINESS

✌ 9 ✌

MEDICINE

❧ II ❧

RISKS AND CONSEQUENCES

13

TOTO

Marietta D. Moskin
illustrated by Rocco Negri

Deep in Africa, on the outer slopes of a gently rolling ring of hills, lived a timid young boy named Suku. His round thatched hut stood in a busy village where his tribe had always lived. Just a short distance away, on the other side of the blue and purple hills, was a quiet valley set aside for animals to live without fear of being

hunted by men. Suku had often climbed to the top of the
tallest hill and had watched the herds of animals moving
through the grasslands far below. But that was as far as he
ever went. His own world was outside the protected game
reserve—with his family, in the safe, familiar village.

On a saucer-shaped plain sheltered by the ring of blue
and purple hills lived a curious little elephant. His name
was Toto—the little one—because he was the youngest and
smallest elephant in the herd. With his large family he
roamed across the silvery plains of his valley, feeding on the
juicy grasses and bathing in the broad green river that twisted through the land. It was a good life for elephants and for
the many other animals with whom they shared their
peaceful valley.

Day by day the little elephant in the valley and the boy
in the village grew stronger and bigger and learned the
things they had to know.

Toto learned which berries and roots were good to eat
and which ones would make him sick. He learned to recognize danger by smells in the air and sounds in the distance. He stood patiently while his mother doused him
with water from her trunk, and he paid attention when she
showed him how to powder himself with red dust to keep
the insects away.

When his mother warned him never to stray outside
their peaceful valley because there were dangers beyond the

hills, Toto listened. Most of the time he was happy to play with his cousins among the thorn trees and with his friends, the antelope and the baby baboons. But sometimes Toto looked toward the blue and purple hills in the distance and wondered what lay behind their rounded crests.

Suku too learned a great many things a boy growing up in an African village had to learn. He carried water for his mother from the river and he collected dung to burn in the fire on which she cooked their midday meal. In the evening he helped his father and the other men to pen the tribe's cattle and goats within the village compound. But in the morning, when the boys and young men of the village went out to herd their cattle on the rich grazing lands in the valley, Suku did not go with them. He watched when the herd boys walked jauntily out of the village, brandishing their wooden staffs and shouting to their charges. At seven he was old enough to go, but Suku was frightened when he thought of the herd boys walking through the bush with nothing but a stick or crude iron spear to protect them from lions.

"Our ancestors were famous lion hunters," his mother scolded. "The men of our tribe have always walked fearlessly through the bush."

"Give Suku time," his father counseled. "Courage sometimes comes with need."

So Suku went on doing women's chores around the village and avoiding the boys who teased him.

And inside the ring of gently rolling purple hills, Toto, the little elephant, roamed with the herd across the grasslands. But whenever he saw the young weaverbirds flying from their hanging straw nests, he watched enviously as they sailed off into the sky far, far beyond the circle of hills.

One night Toto followed the elephant herd to the edge of their valley where the river flowed onto the plain through a gap in the hills. There, in a clearing between the trees, the young males of the herd fought mock battles with each other in the moonlight.

Sheltered by his mother's bulk, Toto watched for a while. Then, looking up at the velvety sky, he saw that the moon had traveled across the valley and was about to dip down below the highest hill.

I wonder where she goes, Toto thought. Perhaps I'll just follow the river a little ways and see. Not very far—just to where the river curves.

Slowly Toto moved away from the group of elephants. Nobody noticed. Not even his mother. But once he was in the shadows of trees, the moon was no longer there to guide him.

"Elephants have no enemies—Mother said so," he told himself bravely. Only the lion might stalk an unprotected elephant child—but the lions had had their kill earlier that night. Toto had seen them at their meal.

Toto walked on through the darkness. Sometimes he could see the moon reflected on the river, and he hurried to

catch up with it. But he didn't look back, and so he didn't realize that the hills lay behind him now. He didn't notice either that he could no longer hear the loud trumpeting of the other elephants at play. He didn't know that he was already in that mysterious world beyond the hills he had longed to discover.

Suddenly Toto felt a sharp pain in his right front leg. Something hard and sharp had fastened around his foot. Toto pulled and pulled, but he couldn't free his foot. Each time he pulled, the pain got sharper.

Nothing his mother had told him about danger had prepared Toto for this. In fear and pain he trumpeted loudly. But he had walked too far to be heard. There was no answering call from his mother or from any of the other elephants. For the first time in his life, Toto was alone.

In the round thatched hut in the village, Suku slept on a woven mat next to his parents. Suku was a sound sleeper, but something—some noise—awoke him before dawn. It sounded like an elephant trumpeting, Suku thought sleepily. But elephants rarely strayed this far out of the game reserve in the valley. He must have been dreaming, Suku told himself. He couldn't have heard an elephant this close.

But Suku could not go back to sleep. When the first sunshine crept through the chinks under the door, he got up and slipped into his clothes. He had promised his mother he would cut some papyrus reeds at the river today so that she could mend their torn sleeping mats. Now that he was awake he would do it before the day grew hot.

Quietly, so as not to waken the rest of his family, Suku tiptoed out of the hut. Outside, no one stirred. Even the cattle were still asleep.

Clutching his sharp reed knife, Suku followed the winding path down the hill to the riverbank, searching for a good stand of feathery papyrus.

Suddenly the silence at the river was broken by a loud rustling sound. The sound came again—not just a rustling this time, but a snapping of twigs and a swishing of the tall grasses. Carefully, and a little fearfully, Suku moved around the next curve in the path. And then he stopped again.

Before him, in the trampled grass, lay a very young elephant. Around one of the elephant's legs the cruelly stiffened

rope of a poacher's trap had been pulled so tight that the
snare had bitten deeply into the flesh. The elephant had
put up a fierce struggle, but now he was exhausted. He lay
quietly on his side, squealing softly from time to time.

Anger exploded inside Suku—anger at the cruel poachers who had set their cunning trap so close to the game
reserve. He approached the trapped elephant carefully. His
father had taught him to be aware of wounded animals who
could be far more dangerous in fear and pain. But the little
elephant seemed to sense that Suku wanted to help him,

and he held very still. Grasping his knife, Suku slashed at the thick, twisted rope. It took time to free the elephant's leg, but finally the last strand of the rope gave way. The boy jumped out of the way quickly, and the small elephant slowly got to his feet. Then he just stood there on the path, staring at Suku.

"Shoo, shoo, little elephant—quickly, run back into the valley," Suku urged. The poachers who had set the trap could be back at any time. But Toto, who had spent the night by himself, would not leave that strange two-legged creature with the oddly dangerous smell but the warm, comforting sounds. When Suku turned to walk back to the village, Toto started after him.

"Please, little one, please, hurry home," Suku pleaded.

But the little elephant didn't budge.

"What are we going to do?" Suku asked in despair. "Will I have to lead you back to your family, you foolish little one?"

Suku didn't want to go into the bush. But he looked at the elephant baby and knew that there was no choice.

Suku began to walk, and the small elephant followed. He walked slowly and painfully, limping on the leg that had been cut so badly by the poacher's snare.

It was easy for Suku to find the way Toto had left the reserve. Trampled grass and elephant droppings formed a perfect track. After a while the boy and the elephant came to the clearing where the herd had watched the fight between the young bulls the night before. The clearing

was empty, but a trail of droppings showed that the herd had moved on across the open bush.

Suku was so busy following the trail that he hadn't thought much about what he was doing. Suddenly he realized he was walking all by himself across the open grasslands. Just like the herd boys. And he didn't even have an iron spear for protection—nothing but a small reed cutting knife!

He walked on, trying not to think about the dangers. By now the sun was high in the sky, and at home they were surely wondering what had happened to him.

They walked and walked. Suku, who hadn't had any breakfast that morning, began to feel hungry and thirsty. Toto hadn't had breakfast either, but there was no time to stop and eat.

Suddenly Toto stopped. He raised his head and listened, trembling a little. Young as he was, Toto recognized the smells and sounds of danger.

Suku looked around to see what had frightened Toto. And then he saw the danger too. A few paces away, half-hidden in the silvery-tan grass, stood an enormous brown-maned lion.

The lion looked from the elephant to the boy, almost as if he were measuring which one would make the easier victim. He looked haughty and strong and very big. Suku's fist tightened around the handle of his knife. He wasn't sure at all whether the knife would do him any good, but he was prepared to defend himself if the lion attacked. Behind him he could sense the little elephant stiffen. Even though the lion looked awfully big to him too, Toto had raised his trunk and spread his ears the way the big elephants did when they were ready to attack.

"Oh, please, make him go away, make him go away," Suku prayed silently. His hand around the knife handle felt clammy and stiff. It seemed to him that he and the elephant and the lion had stood there facing one another, forever.

It was Toto who broke the silence. He took a step toward the lion, and he trumpeted a warning.

The next moment—almost like an echo—another elephant call sounded across the bush. Then another and another. Turning his head, Suku saw a large herd of elephants advancing from behind a nearby stand of thorn trees. Toto's family had come to rescue their littlest one!

Then Suku heard another, more familiar sound. It was the rattling and roaring sound of a car traveling fast across rough ground. A second later the game warden's battered white Landrover appeared over the next small hill. Suku recognized the warden at the wheel, and next to the warden Suku saw his father standing up in the car with a gun in his hand.

"Stand still, Suku—just don't move," his father shouted. He aimed his gun at the lion, waiting to see what the lion would do.

The lion looked at his two young victims. Then he looked at the menacing group of elephants on his right and at the men in the car to his left. Mustering what dignity he could, he stalked slowly and deliberately away. Within moments he had disappeared into the tall dry grass.

Another loud, single call sounded from the elephant herd. Toto was being summoned. His mother was coming to take him back to the herd.

Slowly Toto raised his trunk to the boy who had brought him home. Then, still limping badly, he turned and followed his mother.

The warden had waited for the elephants to withdraw. Now he drove the Landrover over to where Suku stood.

"Get in, Suku—let's go," the warden said.

"You came just in time," Suku said.

"We found the cut snare and the elephant tracks—and someone in the village had seen you going down to the river early this morning," his father explained.

"The poachers would have killed him for his hide," Suku said.

"You did right, Suku," the warden said. "I get so angry too when I catch these poachers. You would make a good game ranger some day, Suku. You love animals, and you are brave."

The warden's words made Suku feel good. He knew that he hadn't felt brave, but he had walked in the footsteps of his ancestors: he had gone into the bush, and he had faced a lion!

Now he would never feel shy of the village boys again. He knew he had earned his place in the tribe.

Under the leafy canopy of the forest, Toto nuzzled up close to his mother's flank. He had eaten his fill of crisp greens at the riverbank, and his mother had bathed his cut foot and smeared it with healing red mud. Now the herd was resting quietly in the shade near the river.

It was good to be back home, Toto thought contentedly. Let the moon and the sun and the birds travel beyond the hills if they wished. His place was here.

MEET MARIETTA MOSKIN, AUTHOR

Marietta Moskin was born in Austria, grew up in Holland, and taught herself English by reading books in an English-language library run by the British Red Cross in Germany after World War II. She finished high school in the United States and has written books in several languages. "I can't remember a time when I didn't want to write poems or stories. During World War II we spent several years in a number of concentration camps where I continued to spin a fantasy world of poetry and stories for myself on hoarded scraps of paper. In my books I have tried to draw as often as possible on my own experiences and remembered feelings. I hope that I can help my readers to expand their horizons and make them understand, through my words, different ways of living, different emotions, circumstances different from their own. This reaching out and sharing is to me one of the great joys of writing for young people." The story of Toto grew out of a trip Moskin took with her family to Kenya, Tanzania, and Uganda, in East Africa.

SARAH, PLAIN AND TALL

Patricia MacLachlan
illustrated by Julie Ecklund

"Did Mama sing every day?" asked Caleb. "Every-single-day?" He sat close to the fire, his chin in his hand. It was dusk, and the dogs lay beside him on the warm hearthstones.

"Every-single-day," I told him for the second time this week. For the twentieth time this month. The hundredth time this year? And the past few years?

"And did Papa sing, too?"

"Yes. Papa sang, too. Don't get so close, Caleb. You'll heat up."

He pushed his chair back. It made a hollow scraping sound on the hearthstones, and the dogs stirred. Lottie, small and black, wagged her tail and lifted her head. Nick slept on.

I turned the bread dough over and over on the marble slab on the kitchen table.

"Well, Papa doesn't sing anymore," said Caleb very softly. A log broke apart and crackled in the fireplace. He looked up at me. "What did I look like when I was born?"

"You didn't have any clothes on," I told him.

"I know that," he said.

"You looked like this." I held the bread dough up in a round pale ball.

"I had hair," said Caleb seriously.

"Not enough to talk about," I said.

"And she named me Caleb," he went on, filling in the old familiar story.

"*I* would have named you Troublesome," I said, making Caleb smile.

"And Mama handed me to you in the yellow blanket and said . . . ." He waited for me to finish the story. "And said . . . ?"

I sighed. "And Mama said, 'Isn't he beautiful, Anna?' "

"And I was," Caleb finished.

Caleb thought the story was over, and I didn't tell him what I had really thought. He was homely and plain, and he had a terrible holler and a horrid smell. But these were not the worst of him. Mama died the next morning. That was the worst thing about Caleb.

"Isn't he beautiful, Anna?" Her last words to me. I had gone to bed thinking how wretched he looked. And I forgot to say good night.

I wiped my hands on my apron and went to the window. Outside, the prairie reached out and touched the places where the sky came down. Though winter was nearly over, there were patches of snow and ice everywhere. I looked at the long dirt road that crawled across the plains, remembering the morning that Mama had died, cruel and sunny. They had come for her in a wagon and taken her away to be buried. And then the cousins and aunts and uncles had come and tried to fill up the house. But they couldn't.

Slowly, one by one, they left. And then the days seemed long and dark like winter days, even though it wasn't winter. And Papa didn't sing.

Isn't he beautiful, Anna?

No, Mama.

It was hard to think of Caleb as beautiful. It took three whole days for me to love him, sitting in the chair by the fire, Papa washing up the supper dishes, Caleb's tiny hand brushing my cheek. And a smile. It was the smile, I know.

"Can you remember her songs?" asked Caleb. "Mama's songs?"

I turned from the window. "No. Only that she sang about flowers and birds. Sometimes about the moon at nighttime."

Caleb reached down and touched Lottie's head.

"Maybe," he said, his voice low, "if you remember the songs, then I might remember her, too."

My eyes widened and tears came. Then the door opened and wind blew in with Papa, and I went to stir the stew. Papa put his arms around me and put his nose in my hair.

"Nice soapy smell, that stew," he said.

I laughed. "That's my hair."

Caleb came over and threw his arms around Papa's neck and hung down as Papa swung him back and forth, and the dogs sat up.

"Cold in town," said Papa. "And Jack was feisty." Jack was Papa's horse that he'd raised from a colt. "Rascal," murmured

Papa, smiling, because no matter what Jack did Papa loved him.

I spooned up the stew and lighted the oil lamp and we ate with the dogs crowding under the table, hoping for spills or handouts.

Papa might not have told us about Sarah that night if Caleb hadn't asked him the question. After the dishes were cleared and washed and Papa was filling the tin pail with ashes, Caleb spoke up. It wasn't a question, really.

"You don't sing anymore," he said. He said it harshly. Not because he meant to, but because he had been thinking of it for so long. "Why?" he asked more gently.

Slowly Papa straightened up. There was a long silence, and the dogs looked up, wondering at it.

"I've forgotten the old songs," said Papa quietly. He sat down. "But maybe there's a way to remember them." He looked up at us.

"How?" asked Caleb eagerly.

Papa leaned back in the chair. "I've placed an advertisement in the newspapers. For help."

"You mean a housekeeper?" I asked, surprised.

Caleb and I looked at each other and burst out laughing, remembering Hilly, our old housekeeper. She was round and slow and shuffling. She snored in a high whistle at night, like a teakettle, and let the fire go out.

"No," said Papa slowly. "Not a housekeeper." He paused. "A wife."

Caleb stared at Papa. "A wife? You mean a mother?"

Nick slid his face onto Papa's lap and Papa stroked his ears.

"That, too," said Papa. "Like Maggie."

Matthew, our neighbor to the south, had written to ask for a wife and mother for his children. And Maggie had come from Tennessee. Her hair was the color of turnips and she laughed.

Papa reached into his pocket and unfolded a letter written on white paper. "And I have received an answer." Papa read to us:

"Dear Mr. Jacob Witting,

"I am Sarah Wheaton from Maine as you will see from my letter. I am answering your advertisement. I have never been married, though I have been asked. I have lived with an older brother, William, who is about to be married. His wife-to-be is young and energetic.

"I have always loved to live by the sea, but at this time I feel a move is necessary. And the truth is, the sea is as far east as I can go. My choice, as you can see, is limited. This should not be taken as an insult. I am strong and I work hard and I am willing to travel. But I am not mild mannered. If you should still care to write, I would be interested in your children and about where you live. And you.

"Very truly yours,

"Sarah Elisabeth Wheaton

"P.S. Do you have opinions on cats? I have one."

No one spoke when Papa finished the letter. He kept looking at it in his hands, reading it over to himself. Finally I turned my head a bit to sneak a look at Caleb. He was smiling. I smiled, too.

"One thing," I said in the quiet of the room.

"What's that?" asked Papa, looking up.

I put my arm around Caleb.

"Ask her if she sings," I said.

Caleb and Papa and I wrote letters to Sarah, and before the ice and snow had melted from the fields, we all received answers. Mine came first.

Dear Anna,

Yes, I can braid hair and I can make stew and bake bread, though I prefer to build bookshelves and paint.

My favorite colors are the colors of the sea, blue and gray and green, depending on the weather. My brother William is a fisherman, and he tells me that when he is in the middle of a fogbound sea the water is a color for which there is no name. He catches flounder and sea bass and bluefish. Sometimes he sees whales. And birds, too, of course. I am enclosing a book of sea birds so you will see what William and I see every day.

Very truly yours,

Sarah Elisabeth Wheaton

Caleb read and read the letter so many times that the ink began to run and the folds tore. He read the book about sea birds over and over.

"Do you think she'll come?" asked Caleb. "And will she stay? What if she thinks we are loud and pesky?"

"You *are* loud and pesky," I told him. But I was worried, too. Sarah loved the sea, I could tell. Maybe she wouldn't leave there after all to come where there were fields and grass and sky and not much else.

"What if she comes and doesn't like our house?" Caleb asked. "I told her it was small. Maybe I shouldn't have told her it was small."

"Hush, Caleb. Hush."

Caleb's letter came soon after, with a picture of a cat drawn on the envelope.

Dear Caleb,

My cat's name is Seal because she is gray like the seals that swim offshore in Maine. She is glad that Lottie and Nick send their greetings. She likes dogs most of the time. She says their footprints are much larger than hers (which she is enclosing in return).

Your house sounds lovely, even though it is far out in the country with no close neighbors. My house is tall and the shingles are gray because of the salt from the sea. There are roses nearby.

Yes, I do like small rooms sometimes. Yes, I can keep a fire going at night. I do not know if I snore. Seal has never told me.

Very truly yours,
Sarah Elisabeth

"Did you really ask her about fires and snoring?" I asked, amazed.

"I wished to know," Caleb said.

He kept the letter with him, reading it in the barn and in the fields and by the cow pond. And always in bed at night.

One morning, early, Papa and Caleb and I were cleaning out the horse stalls and putting down new bedding. Papa stopped suddenly and leaned on his pitchfork.

"Sarah has said she will come for a month's time if we wish her to," he said, his voice loud in the dark barn. "To see how it is. Just to see."

Caleb stood by the stall door and folded his arms across his chest.

"I think," he began. Then, "I think," he said slowly, "that it would be good—to say yes," he finished in a rush.

Papa looked at me.

"I say yes," I told him, grinning.

"Yes," said Papa. "Then yes it is."

And the three of us, all smiling, went to work again.

The next day Papa went to town to mail his letter to Sarah. It was rainy for days, and the clouds followed. The house was cool and damp and quiet. Once I set four places at the table, then caught myself and put the extra plate away. Three lambs were born, one with a black face. And then Papa's letter came. It was very short.

Dear Jacob,
  I will come by train. I will wear a yellow bonnet. I am plain and tall.
  Sarah

"What's that?" asked Caleb excitedly, peering over Papa's shoulder. He pointed. "There, written at the bottom of the letter."

Papa read it to himself. Then he smiled, holding up the letter for us to see.

Tell them I sing was all it said.

Sarah came in the spring. She came through green grass fields that bloomed with Indian paintbrush, red and orange, and blue-eyed grass.

Papa got up early for the long day's trip to the train and back. He brushed his hair so slick and shiny that Caleb laughed. He wore a clean blue shirt, and a belt instead of suspenders.

He fed and watered the horses, talking to them as he hitched them up to the wagon. Old Bess, calm and kind; Jack, wild-eyed, reaching over to nip Bess on the neck.

"Clear day, Bess," said Papa, rubbing her nose.

"Settle down, Jack." He leaned his head on Jack.

And then Papa drove off along the dirt road to fetch Sarah. Papa's new wife. Maybe. Maybe our new mother.

Gophers ran back and forth across the road, stopping to stand up and watch the wagon. Far off in the field a wood-chuck ate and listened. Ate and listened.

Caleb and I did our chores without talking. We shov-eled out the stalls and laid down new hay. We fed the sheep. We swept and straightened and carried wood and water. And then our chores were done.

Caleb pulled on my shirt.

"Is my face clean?" he asked. "Can my face be *too* clean?" He looked alarmed.

"No, your face is clean but not too clean," I said.

Caleb slipped his hand into mine as we stood on the porch, watching the road. He was afraid.

"Will she be nice?" he asked. "Like Maggie?"

"Sarah will be nice," I told him.

"How far away is Maine?" he asked.

"You know how far. Far away, by the sea."

"Will Sarah bring some sea?" he asked.

"No, you cannot bring the sea."

The sheep ran in the field, and far off the cows moved slowly to the pond, like turtles.

"Will she like us?" asked Caleb very softly.

I watched a marsh hawk wheel down behind the barn.

He looked up at me.

"Of course she will like us." He answered his own question. "We are nice," he added, making me smile.

We waited and watched. I rocked on the porch and Caleb rolled a marble on the wood floor. Back and forth. Back and forth. The marble was blue.

We saw the dust from the wagon first, rising above the road, above the heads of Jack and Old Bess. Caleb climbed up onto the porch roof and shaded his eyes.

"A bonnet!" he cried. "I see a yellow bonnet!"

The dogs came out from under the porch, ears up, their eyes on the cloud of dust bringing Sarah. The wagon passed the fenced field, and the cows and sheep looked up, too. It rounded the windmill and the barn and the windbreak of Russian olive that Mama had planted long ago. Nick began to bark, then Lottie, and the wagon clattered into the yard and stopped by the steps.

"Hush," said Papa to the dogs.

And it was quiet.

Sarah stepped down from the wagon, a cloth bag in her hand. She reached up and took off her yellow bonnet, smoothing back her brown hair into a bun. She was plain and tall.

"Did you bring some sea?" cried Caleb beside me.

"Something from the sea," said Sarah, smiling. "And me." She turned and lifted a black case from the wagon. "And Seal, too."

Carefully she opened the case, and Seal, gray with white feet, stepped out. Lottie lay down, her head on her paws, staring. Nick leaned down to sniff. Then he lay down, too.

"The cat will be good in the barn," said Papa. "For mice."

Sarah smiled. "She will be good in the house, too."

Sarah took Caleb's hand, then mine. Her hands were large and rough. She gave Caleb a shell—a moon snail, she called it—that was curled and smelled of salt.

"The gulls fly high and drop the shells on the rocks below," she told Caleb. "When the shell is broken, they eat what is inside."

"That is very smart," said Caleb.

"For you, Anna," said Sarah, "a sea stone."

And she gave me the smoothest and whitest stone I had ever seen.

"The sea washes over and over and around the stone, rolling it until it is round and perfect."

"That is very smart, too," said Caleb. He looked up at Sarah. "We do not have the sea here."

Sarah turned and looked out over the plains.

"No," she said. "There is no sea here. But the land rolls a little like the sea."

My father did not see her look, but I did. And I knew that Caleb had seen it, too. Sarah was not smiling. Sarah was already lonely. In a month's time the preacher might come to marry Sarah and Papa. And a month was a long time. Time enough for her to change her mind and leave us.

Papa took Sarah's bags inside, where her room was ready with a quilt on the bed and blue flax dried in a vase on the night table.

Seal stretched and made a small cat sound. I watched her circle the dogs and sniff the air. Caleb came out and stood beside me.

"When will we sing?" he whispered.

I shook my head, turning the white stone over and over in my hand. I wished everything was as perfect as the stone. I wished that Papa and Caleb and I were perfect for Sarah. I wished we had a sea of our own.

MEET PATRICIA MACLACHLAN, AUTHOR

In her Newbery Award acceptance speech Patricia MacLachlan explained how Sarah, Plain and Tall *came out of her past and was sparked by a trip she took with her family to the prairies. "*Sarah, Plain and Tall *grew out of . . . what my mother used to call the heroics of a common life. My mother told me early on about the real Sarah, who came from the coast of Maine to the prairie to become a wife and mother to a close family member. My mother remembered her fondly. So the facts of Sarah were there for years, though the book began, as books often do, when the past stepped on the heels of the present. Two of my children began to prepare to leave home for college. But before they left, my parents took us on a trip west to the prairie, where they and I had been born. It was a gift for all of us, for the children to see a land they had never seen, to know family they had never met, to stand on the vast North Dakota farm where my father had been born in a sod house, and as Anna observes, 'the prairie reached out and touched the places where the sky came down.' "*

MRS. FRISBY AND THE CROW

from Mrs. Frisby and the Rats of NIMH by Robert C. O'Brien
illustrated by Barbara Lanza

Mrs. Frisby is a mouse that lives with her children in a country garden. When her son Timothy becomes ill, she undertakes a treacherous journey to bring him some medicine.

Mrs. Frisby looked again at the sun and saw that she faced an unpleasant choice. She could go home by the same roundabout way she had come, in which case she would surely end up walking alone in the woods in the dark—a frightening prospect, for at night the forest was alive with danger. Then the owl came out to hunt, and foxes, weasels and strange wild cats stalked among the tree trunks.

The other choice would be dangerous, too, but with luck it would get her home before dark. That would be to take a straighter route, across the farmyard between the barn and the chicken house, going not too close to the house but cutting the distance home by half. The cat would be there somewhere, but by daylight—and by staying in the open, away from the shrubs—she could probably spot him before he saw her.

The cat: He was called Dragon. Farmer Fitzgibbon's wife had given him the name as a joke when he was a small kitten pretending to be fierce. But when he grew up, the name turned out to be an apt one. He was enormous, with a huge, broad head and a large mouth full of curving fangs, needle sharp. He had seven claws on each foot and a thick, furry tail, which lashed angrily from side to side. In color he was orange and white, with glaring yellow eyes; and when he leaped to kill, he gave a high, strangled scream that froze his victims where they stood.

But Mrs. Frisby preferred not to think about that. Instead, as she came out of the woods from Mr. Ages' house and reached the farmyard fence she thought about Timothy. She thought of how his eyes shone with merriment when he made up small jokes, which he did frequently, and how invariably kind he was to his small, scatterbrained sister Cynthia. The other children sometimes laughed at her when she made mistakes, or grew impatient with her because she was forever losing things; but Timothy never did. Instead, he would help her find them. And when

Cynthia herself had been sick in bed with a cold, he had sat by her side for hours and entertained her with stories. He made these up out of his head, and he seemed to have a bottomless supply of them.

Taking a firm grip on her packets of medicine, Mrs. Frisby went under the fence and set out toward the farmyard. The first stretch was a long pasture; the barn itself, square and red and big, rose in the distance to her right; to her left, farther off, were the chicken houses.

When at length she came abreast of the barn, she saw the cattle wire fence that marked the other end of the pasture; and as she approached it, she was startled by a sudden outburst of noise. She thought at first it was a hen, strayed from the chicken yard—caught by a fox? She looked down the fence and saw that it was no hen at all, but a young crow, flapping in the grass, acting most odd. As she watched, he fluttered to the top wire of the fence, where he perched nervously for a moment. Then he spread his wings, flapped hard, and took off—but after flying four feet he stopped with a snap and crashed to the ground again, shedding a flurry of black feathers and squawking loudly.

He was tied to the fence. A piece of something silvery— it looked like wire—was tangled around one of his legs; the other end of it was caught in the fence. Mrs. Frisby walked closer, and then she could see it was not wire after all, but a length of silver-colored string, probably left over from a Christmas package.

The crow was sitting on the fence, pecking ineffectively at the string with his bill, cawing softly to himself, a miserable sound. After a moment he spread his wings, and she could see he was going to try to fly again.

"Wait," said Mrs. Frisby.

The crow looked down and saw her in the grass.

"Why should I wait? Can't you see I'm caught? I've got to get loose."

"But if you make so much noise again the cat is sure to hear. If he hasn't heard already."

"You'd make noise, too, if you were tied to a fence with a piece of string, and with night coming on."

"I would not," said Mrs. Frisby, "if I had any sense and knew there was a cat nearby. Who tied you?" She was trying to calm the crow, who was obviously terrified.

He looked embarrassed and stared at his feet. "I picked up the string. It got tangled with my foot. I sat on the fence to try to get it off, and it caught on the fence."

"*Why* did you pick up the string?"

The crow, who was very young indeed—in fact, only a year old—said wearily, "Because it was shiny."

"You knew better."

"I had been told."

Birdbrain, thought Mrs. Frisby, and then recalled what her husband used to say: The size of the brain is no measure of its capacity. And well she might recall it, for the crow's head was double the size of her own.

"Sit quietly," she said. "Look toward the house and see if you see the cat."

"I don't see him. But I can't see behind the bushes. Oh, if I could just fly higher . . ."

"Don't," said Mrs. Frisby. She looked at the sun; it was setting behind the trees. She thought of Timothy, and of the medicine she was carrying. Yet she knew she could not leave the foolish crow there to be killed—and killed he surely would be before sunrise—just for want of a few minutes' work. She might still make it by dusk if she hurried.

"Come down here," she said. "I'll get the string off."

"How?" said the crow dubiously.

"Don't argue. I have only a few minutes." She said this in a voice so authoritative that the crow fluttered down immediately.

"But if the cat comes . . ." he said.

"If the cat comes, he'll knock you off the fence with one jump and catch you with the next. Be still." She was already at work with her sharp teeth, gnawing at the string. It was twined and twisted and twined again around his right ankle, and she saw she would have to cut through it three times to get it off.

As she finished the second strand, the crow, who was staring toward the house, suddenly cried out:

"I see the cat!"

"*Quiet!*" whispered Mrs. Frisby. "Does he see us?"

"I don't know. Yes. He's looking at me. I don't think he can see you."

"Stand perfectly still. Don't get in a panic." She did not look up, but started on the third strand.

"He's moving this way."

"Fast or slow?"

"Medium. I think he's trying to figure out what I'm doing."

She cut through the last strand, gave a tug, and the string fell off.

"There, you're free. Fly off, and be quick."

"But what about you?"

"Maybe he hasn't seen me."

"But he will. He's coming closer."

Mrs. Frisby looked around. There was not a bit of cover anywhere near, not a rock nor a hole nor a log; nothing at all closer than the chicken yard—and that was in the direction the cat was coming from, and a long way off.

"Look," said the crow. "Climb on my back. Quick. And hang on."

Mrs. Frisby did what she was told, first grasping the precious packages of medicine tightly between her teeth.

"Are you on?"

"Yes."

She gripped the feathers on his back, felt the beat of his powerful black wings, felt a dizzying upward surge, and shut her eyes tight.

"Just in time," said the crow, and she heard the angry scream of the cat as he leaped at where they had just been. "It's lucky you're so light. I can scarcely tell you're there."

Lucky indeed, thought Mrs. Frisby; if it had not been for your foolishness, I'd never have gotten into such a scrape. However, she thought it wise not to say so, under the circumstances.

"Where do you live?" asked the crow.

"In the garden patch. Near the big stone."

"I'll drop you off there." He banked alarmingly, and for a moment Mrs. Frisby thought he meant it literally. But a few seconds later—so fast does the crow fly—they were gliding to earth a yard from her front door.

"Thank you very much," said Mrs. Frisby, hopping to the ground.

"It's I who should be thanking you," said the crow. "You saved my life."

"And you mine."

"Ah, but that's not quite even. Yours wouldn't have been risked if it had not been for me—me and my piece of string." And since this was just what she had been thinking, Mrs. Frisby did not argue.

"We all help one another against the cat," she said.

"True. Just the same, I am in debt to you. If the time ever comes when I can help you, I hope you will ask me. My name is Jeremy. Mention it to any crow you see in these woods, and he will find me."

"Thank you," said Mrs. Frisby. "I will remember."

Jeremy flew away to the woods, and she entered her house, taking the three doses of medicine with her.

MEET ROBERT C. O'BRIEN, AUTHOR

Robert C. O'Brien, born Robert Leslie Conly, describes how he came up with the idea for his Newbery Award–winning book, Mrs. Frisby and the Rats of NIMH. *"I wondered what animals would survive if all humans vanished from the earth. Thinking about survival, I began to speculate: Rats are tough, highly adaptable to a changing environment, and enormously prolific. Maybe if people should eliminate one another by means of war or pollution, rats would be the survivors. Or if not the only survivors perhaps the most intelligent. What then would a rat civilization be like? . . . It was this kind of speculation that led to the birth of* Mrs. Frisby and the Rats of NIMH.*"*

THE KING'S FOUNTAIN

Lloyd Alexander
illustrated by Ezra Jack Keats

A king once planned to build a magnificent fountain in his palace gardens, for the splendor of his kingdom and the glory of his name.

This fountain, however, would stop all water from flowing to the city below.

A poor man heard of it, and said to his wife:

"Soon our children will cry for water, our animals will sicken, and all of us will die of thirst."

His wife answered:

"A man of highest learning must go to the King, speak to him out of wisdom, and show him the folly of his plan."

So the poor man went throughout the city, to the most learned of scholars, and begged him to plead the cause.

But the scholar, deep in his own grand thoughts, barely listened. He pondered lofty matters and had no interest in humbler ones.

And the scholar lectured him with so many cloudy words that the poor man could make no sense of them at all, and went away downcast, saying to himself:

"Alas, the grandest thought quenches no thirst. Besides, what good is all the learning in the world if there is no one who can understand it?"

He realized that someone must present the cause clearly and winningly, with a golden tongue, so the King would listen and agree.

So he went to the marketplace, to the merchants whose words were smooth as pearls and who could string them together endlessly.

But when these merchants heard what he wanted, they choked with fear and their glib words failed them. While they gladly offered clever advice, not one dared face the King.

The poor man left them and went away dismayed, saying to himself:

"Alas, the finest words are empty air without the deeds to fill them. Besides, what good is a golden tongue without a brave heart?"

Then he realized that a man of strength and courage must go and force the King to change his plan.

Again he went throughout the city, to the strongest of all brave men: a fearless metalsmith who could knot an iron bar as easily as a shoestring.

The metalsmith, eager to stand against the King, swore that once inside the palace he would smash every window, crack every wall, and break the King's throne into firewood.

The poor man sadly shook his head, knowing the palace guards would strike down the rash metalsmith before he did even one of those deeds. And the King in his wrath would be all the more determined to build his fountain. So, leaving the metalsmith still pounding his fists, he went away in despair, saying to himself:

"Alas, the strongest hand is useless without a wise head to guide it. Besides, what good is all the bravery in the world if it serves no purpose?"

56

He trudged home, hopeless and heavy-hearted, and told his neighbors and his family that he could find no one to stop the building of the fountain.

His daughter spoke then, and said:

"But, Father—why not go yourself?"

Confused, unable to answer, the poor man looked at the faces of his wife and family. At last, he bowed his head and murmured:

"I hear my own flesh and blood. Indeed, there is no one else, and I must must go to the King."

The poor man left his home. Alone, he slowly climbed the steep and seemingly endless hill.

Finally, he reached the King's high palace and for a long while stood outside, fearful and hesitant.

When the palace guards roughly seized him and threatened his life for intruding, the poor man trembled in such

terror he could scarcely speak. Desperately he blurted out that he had an important message for the King alone.

The guards marched him to the throne room, where the King angrily demanded why he had come.

Knees knocking, teeth chattering, the poor man began to tell as well as he could of the suffering that the fountain would cause.

"Enough!" roared the King. "How dare you question what I do? I am the King!"

The poor man wished for the smallest crumb of the scholar's learning, but he could only stammer:

"Majesty—thirst is thirst, a poor man's no less than a king's."

Then his tongue dried in his mouth and he wished for even one of the merchants' golden words.

The King looked scornfully at him. "You come to trouble me for that? I need only snap my fingers and my swordsmen will cut you to pieces and be done with you."

The poor man wished for one drop of the metalsmith's bravery. With his own last ounce of courage, he answered:

"You have the power to kill me. But that changes nothing. Your people will still die of thirst. Remember them each time you see your splendid fountain."

The King started up, ready to call his guards. But he stopped and fell silent for a time, his frowns deep as his thoughts. Then he replied:

"You are too simple for clever debate with me; but you have a wiser head than a scholar. Your speech is halting;

but there is more true eloquence in your words than in the golden tongue of a cunning counselor. You are too weak to crack a flea; but you have a braver heart than anyone in my kingdom. I will do as you ask."

The poor man returned to the city and told the news to all. The scholar wrote a long account of the matter in one of his books, and misplaced it. The merchants never stopped ornamenting tales of the poor man's deed. The metalsmith was so excited he tossed his anvil into the air and broke one of his own windows.

The poor man, glad simply to be home with his rejoicing family, was hardly able to believe what he had done.

"A wise head? A golden tongue? A brave heart?" he said to himself. "Well, no matter. At least none of us will go thirsty."

AMELIA EARHART, FLY ON

from AMELIA EARHART
by Carol Ann Pearce
*illustrated by Mary Beth Schwark
and Bob Kuester*

*In the 1920s and 1930s, aviation was still a young science
and airplanes were crude, unpredictable machines. Flying one
over long distances was a risky business.*

*Amelia Earhart's passion for flying began in 1920,
when she rode in an airplane for the first time at age twenty-
three. Determined to become a pilot, Amelia took a few
lessons, bought a small airplane, and took to the skies.*

*In 1922, Amelia broke the women's altitude record,
climbing 14,000 feet in a 60-horsepower airplane called a
Canary. In 1928, she became the first woman to cross the
Atlantic Ocean in an airplane. Wilmer Stultz piloted the
three-engine plane called the* Friendship, *and Amelia kept a
journal of weather conditions and air speed during the flight.*

*After returning to the United States, Amelia embarked on a
cross-country flight and set another record: first solo
transcontinental flight by a woman going from East Coast to
West Coast and back again. In 1932, she wanted to top this
feat with an even greater flight. Amelia wanted to become the
first woman to fly solo across the Atlantic Ocean.*

Atlantic Solo, May 1932

The project involved a gamble . . . My stake in this
throw . . . was my life against the joy of doing something I wanted to do very much.

AMELIA EARHART

The 1930s saw a burst of activity on the part of
women pilots all over the world as they raced to set
flight records and outdo one another. This must
have put great pressure on Amelia Earhart to do something
outstanding. Here she was a widely touted spokesperson for
aviation while other women accomplished record journeys.
With so many showing daring and courage, Amelia ran a
real danger of being left behind if she didn't find some way
to outdo everyone.

The Great Depression gripped the nation. Millions of people could not find work. Soup kitchens and bread lines were part of the national scene. The entire world was experiencing economic collapse.

Hard times didn't affect Amelia Earhart, though, as she continued toward her goal of pushing on in aviation wherever she found an opening.

Over a four-year period, Amelia had logged nearly a thousand flying hours, many of them on instruments alone. She practiced setting courses, estimating arrival times, then setting out without looking around to check her position on the way. This skill was essential if she were to cross the Atlantic with nothing but the ocean below.

With the help of her husband, George Putnam, Amelia set up a timetable. They decided what had to be done before takeoff day, and agreed to bring in an expert to help prepare her and the airplane for a successful completion of the journey.

Bernt Balchen was their first choice. A flier, explorer, and adventurer, he had accompanied Admiral Byrd to the North and South poles. Marriage to Putnam [owner of a publishing company], as well as fame, gave Amelia the access to such experts as Balchen that many other women did not have.

Balchen came to lunch on one of the first days of spring in 1932. Crocuses bloomed on the lawn where they adjourned for a game of croquet after eating. It was there that Amelia told him what she wanted.

"Will you help me? Am I ready?" she asked.

"Yes," he responded to both questions.

Amelia Earhart in the cockpit of her autogiro after setting a new altitude record for women in planes of this type. April 8, 1931

UPI/Bettmann

Eddie Gorski, Amelia Earhart, and Bernt Balchen before the plane in which Earhart will attempt her transatlantic flight. May 19, 1932

UPI/Bettmann

Criticisms had been leveled about her lack of flying expertise at the time of the *Friendship* trip and shortly after. Her abilities were not at the level of her former flying partner, Wilmer Stultz, a fact she herself pointed out frequently during the hullabaloo that followed her first Atlantic flight as a passenger. This criticism, along with society's attitude that a woman always needed some man at the controls of an airplane, must have made her doubt herself even more. Female pilots were referred to as "fair devotees of flight," implying that they were not equal to men in the air.

Even though Amelia had flown coast to coast without any man's help, placed in a transcontinental air race, and set altitude and speed records, society still regarded women as incapable of real aerial achievements. The public fawned over her for things she considered unimportant, at the same time they downplayed her real accomplishments. By actions, she hoped to let other women see the truth apart from society's opinions.

Her plane needed a new engine. For the long flight without refueling, it needed extra gas tanks. To oversee the work, Balchen had the plane moved to the Teterboro, New Jersey, airport across the Hudson River from New York City and near where he lived. He hired Ed Gorski, engineer and maintenance supervisor for Fokker Aircraft Corporation, to undertake the alterations. Getting the proper fuel mix was crucial. Helping with that project was Army pilot Major

Edwin Aldrin. (In the 1960s, his son Buzz would make America's second voyage to the moon.)

The trip was kept secret in order to give Amelia the freedom to back out at any time, and also so that she could prepare herself mentally without interruptions. Officially the plane was chartered to Balchen to keep her name out of speculations about the work he was performing in connection with the craft.

The plane's flying range with added fuel tanks was 3,200 miles. From Harbour Grace, Newfoundland (the jumping-off point) to Paris, France, would be a distance of 2,640 miles. The added fuel tanks gave Amelia a safety margin of 560 miles, thus allowing some room for headwinds or losing her way.

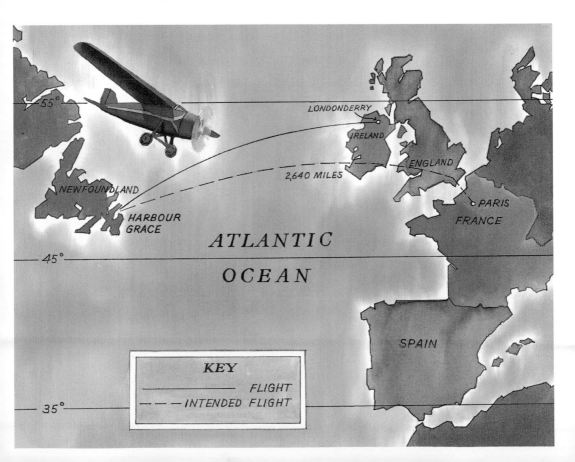

While Balchen worked on the plane, Amelia flew when she could, and visited U.S. Weather Bureau meteorologist Dr. James Kimball at his weather office in Manhattan. His expertise had been crucial to the *Friendship* flight and now, though Amelia didn't reveal her intentions, he cooperated fully with her. Her keen attention to weather patterns in the North Atlantic told him all he needed to know.

Weather would play a big role in this long flight, since planes then were fragile and incapable of flying above storm systems that were miles high. Predicting weather in those days was more guesswork than science, but Kimball did his best with guesses. Sometimes storms over the North Atlantic covered the entire distance between Newfoundland and England.

"The doing of a thing may take little courage," AE [Amelia Earhart] wrote later for *Cosmopolitan Magazine*. "The preparation for it—the acceptance of the inevitable risks involved—may be a far greater test of morale."

Throughout the first part of May, storms raged over the Atlantic keeping her from leaving.

Thursday, May 19. GP [George Putnam] drove to Manhattan. Amelia drove to Teterboro Airport for a routine visit. Fog coated her windshield. The Hudson River lay under a thick haze.

Just before noon, as she prepared to take off for a quick hop in the Vega she would be flying across the Atlantic, a call came. It was GP at Doc Kimball's office. Weather was breaking. It would be clear to fly as far as New Brunswick that day. Then, GP told her, "The Atlantic looks as good as you are likely to get it for some time."

The trip was on. "OK. We'll start."

She raced back to Rye, changed into flying breeches, a windbreaker and leather flying suit. She grabbed $15 in cash, some maps, and a toothbrush. As she hurriedly left the house, the sight of spring flowers struck her. "Those sweet blooms smiled at me a radiant farewell," she wrote later. "That's a memory I have never forgotten." The excitement, the razor's edge of danger, made her senses keen.

Four years of preparation had brought her to this moment when she would be on her own at last, ready to prove to herself—and the world—that she was nobody's phony.

Putnam met her en route and together they drove to Teterboro, arriving at 2:55 P.M. By 3:15 Amelia Earhart, Ed Gorski, and Bernt Balchen were airborne and heading north to New Brunswick, Canada. Balchen flew the plane so that she might rest along the way. After a stopover at St. Johns, New Brunswick, that night, they took off early in the morning of May 20 and flew on to Harbour Grace. From there, when she got the OK from Kimball about the weather, Amelia would be on her own.

Putnam's cables awaited them. A storm system lay to the south. Winds, out of the west, were favorable. That night would be clear, with a moon. There were some clouds 400 miles east.

If Amelia didn't get away that same day, weather might close in again for a long while. "Under these circumstances," she said, "it was harder to wait than to go."

She decided to leave that afternoon.

A 12-motor German flying boat, the *Do-X*, lay at anchor 24 miles away from Harbour Grace in Holyrood on its journey to the Azores off the coast of Portugal, from where it could feed weather information to Harbour Grace. Amelia decided not to wait for that assistance. She wired GP that she would leave at 5:00 P.M., then lay down while Balchen and Gorski gave the plane one last check.

"In anything that requires intelligence, coordination, spirit, coolness and willpower, women can meet men on their own ground," she once said. But words were nothing without proof. She was soloing for all women.

Bernt Balchen warmed up the red plane with the gold stripe down the side. A cable arrived from New York. OK STOP SO LONG STOP GOOD LUCK. GP. This was the language of explorers and adventurers that Amelia and George Putnam shared, an understatement in the face of danger.

Heavily loaded with gasoline, the single-engine Vega would require skilled handling on takeoff. Balchen gave Amelia last-minute instructions: what course to hold, what weather she might expect. Wind ruffled her blond hair. She bit her lip as he talked, anxious to be going. It was close to 7:00 P.M. before she got away. Her beloved Vega waited for its greatest challenge and she hoped she "would not let it down." "Do you think I can make it?" she asked Balchen with what he later described as a "lonely smile."

"You bet," he said firmly. They shook hands. Twilight approached as she climbed into the cockpit of the airplane and started the engine. After checking the instruments, and without glancing from her control panel, Amelia Earhart nodded to Gorski to remove the chocks from the wheels. Slowly the red and gold plane began to roll down the runway, then finally turned, and paused. The vastness of the sky and the ocean beyond lay before this woman whose most distinguishing physical characteristic, according to her husband, was her slimness. The small red plane thundered and shook as the motor revved for takeoff. Then, throttle shoved to the firewall, it came roaring down the runway. The waiting, the preparing were over.

"The plane picked up speed quickly," the New York Times said of her takeoff afterward, "and before it had rolled 2,000 feet down the runway it had left the ground . . . Nursing the engine carefully she climbed and went into a wide turn over Lady Lake and out across town over the blue waters of Conception Bay."

Balchen, Gorski, and airport manager Herman Archibald scrambled up a cliff near the end of the runway to watch the single-engine Vega, NR-7952, with the scarlet tail fin vanish into the distance.

"To . . . do a thing for its own sake, to enjoy doing it, to concentrate all one's energies upon it, that is not only the surest guarantee of its success it is also being true to one-self," she had written.

When George Putnam received word that his wife was on her way, he called a news conference. "PUTNAM SURE OF WIFE'S SUCCESS," the *Times* said. And: "FIRST WOMAN TO MAKE ATTEMPT FACES CLOUDS 400 MILES OUT BUT PLANS TO SOAR OVER THEM."

A reporter asked Putnam how he felt. "As well as could be expected," he replied.

At one hour out, her log notes two icebergs in the water below. Two hours: a small boat. She blinks her lights but gets no response.

In Newfoundland, Gorski and Balchen waited for reports from ships that might have spotted her. They heard nothing. Her estimated arrival time in Paris was 12 to 15 hours after takeoff. There was no means of communication with the plane en route since radios were not part of her plane's equipment at that time.

Sunset over the North Atlantic lasted those first two hours, then the moon rose as clouds began to form below. Suddenly the needle of her altimeter spun. In 12 years of flying, it had never broken before. Now without it, she would have no idea of how high or low she was flying. Ahead, visible in the moonlight, spread a towering mass of black clouds across the horizon as far as she could see. With no way around the approaching storm, Amelia Earhart headed into it. By 11:30 P.M. the moon had vanished, blotted out by blackness. Surrounded by seething black air, her only light came from the dim glow of the instrument panel. The storm struck.

Lightning split the dark as winds knocked the plane about and rain lashed it. The plane bounced and jolted, thrown by violent forces. It was a storm worse than any she had ever encountered. Still, calmly she went about resetting her Sperry gyrocompass every 20 minutes as planned, even though she knew she might already have been blown off course.

At times such as these, she found comfort in doing small, practical tasks.

The moon reappeared at a break in the clouds. Thinking she might be able to get over the turbulence, she began to climb, the plane nosing upward. Temperature in the cockpit dropped rapidly. Slush began to collect on the windshield. Her airspeed indicator turned erratic and began to spin. This meant that ice had to be forming on the wings, making the plane too heavy to overcome the force of gravity. The controls felt sluggish in her hands. A moment later, the plane rolled over and fell toward the earth.

Plummeting through the storm, Amelia Earhart struggled to pull the plane out of its high-speed spin toward the ocean. Down it screamed. How close was the water? How far had she climbed? When would she hit? Picking up speed as it dropped, the Vega fell 3,000 feet, a fact recorded on

the barograph on board, before, at the very last second, she was able to pull it up when she could see whitecaps. There was no time to enjoy her relief. The storm closed in and she could no longer see again, though she knew from that one glimpse that the water couldn't be more than 100 feet below.

"It gave me a queer feeling not being able to know when I was getting too near the water . . . I had to fly low to prevent ice forming but I certainly didn't want to go into the Atlantic."

These experiences would have been enough to make most people turn back, but she flew on, perhaps believing the worst had to be over. What more could happen?

Flames broke out through a crack in the manifold ring. In her book *The Fun of It* she later wrote that she was sorry she noticed the flames because they looked so much worse at night than they would have appeared in the daytime. The plane began to vibrate fiercely, as though any second something was going to break and send her falling into the icy waters. Perilously close to the point of no return, she still had enough gas to take her back to land if she turned around.

It was then, reported the *New York Times*, she made her bravest decision: to fly on. "If she went ahead it meant fighting wind and rain in mid-ocean with a partly crippled engine. She decided to go on."

Actually should she have turned back, she would have been trying to find Newfoundland in the dark, which was chancy, and land in the dark, which was extremely risky. This was a flight she had undertaken with little thought of aborting it along the way.

In the cold and sitting tensely in one position for so long, her feet grew numb at the rudder pedals. The storms continued to buffet her about as she changed compass settings regularly, keeping watch for any signs that she was getting close to the water below.

If the engine didn't fail on her, she decided she still had a *fair* chance of making land the next day.

The forecast turned out dramatically different from what was predicted. Atlantic weather conditions change rapidly. By the time Doc Kimball got reports, they were already old. Though he was as careful and painstaking as possible under the circumstances, there was a wide margin for error. Ironically, the very trouble Amelia waited so long to avoid engulfed her.

Past the point of no return, she continued heading east. Now there was not enough fuel for returning, only enough to take her to her destination. Guessing, she flew what she hoped was high enough to avoid the water, yet low enough to keep ice from forming on the wings.

When interviewed for a women's needlecraft magazine, Amelia had been asked, "Do you spin?" "Surely I spin," she replied, "tail spin—at 4,000 feet."

There was no way for her to rest or sleep. For food, she punched holes in the top of a tomato juice can and sipped at it still unable to see where she was going, as she plowed on through the "soup."

In the night, her fuel gauge broke. Gas leaked down the back of her neck, filling the cockpit with fumes that made her nauseous and her eyes water.

"In moments of danger," she wrote later, "whether you are coward or hero, you do your best."

Without being able to see anything out her windows but turbulent blackness, Amelia Earhart flew on for over 10 hours. Dawn came. The light revealed heavy clouds above and below. Gradually the plane's vibrations had worsened and Amelia did not know, because of the broken gauge, how much fuel she had left.

"Morning was the worst," wrote Amelia's sister Muriel in her book about Amelia's flight, *Courage Is the Price*. "Seeing mirages, seeing 'land' that wasn't there."

The plane shook so hard that Amelia forced herself to give up the notion of trying for Paris. She had to seek out landfall as quickly as she could. Since Kimball's forecast had noted storms to the south of her course, she thought that perhaps she had been blown south into them. Therefore, after giving up on Paris, she altered her course to due east hoping to find Ireland. The plane spewed flames, shaking so hard that at any moment it seemed it might break apart. Having flown out of touch with the world for over 13 hours in violent winds and storms, AE knew she would be very lucky indeed to find any land at all.

Each minute that passed must have been agonizing, because she did not know what the next minute or hour held. When she saw a black line on the horizon, she had to doubt her hopes that it was a shoreline; but as she flew on toward the line, it did not vanish like the dream of a desperate pilot, but grew and grew. It became mountains. It became water breaking on a shore. Railroad tracks finally appeared. These were the last moments of the crossing. Carefully, painstakingly, Amelia Earhart searched the rolling emerald pastureland below her for sight of a smooth, long stretch with no stones, fences, or ditches. As her plane roared overhead, cows scattered. Spotting a meadow, she throttled back to start her descent. Despite the mechanical problems with the airplane and the uneven terrain, she made a perfect landing. The plane rolled to a gentle stop at the top of a slight knoll. Motor switched to off, AE sat back

to let the realization of what she had done seep into her. She had made it. Wherever she was, she surely had crossed the Atlantic.

Dan McCallon, a farmhand, came running to see what the noise was all about.

He couldn't tell if he was talking to a man or woman, since AE's face was greased against the cold, and she wore a flying suit and a leather helmet. Politely he inquired, "Have you flown far?"

"From America," came her dry and probably numb reply.

Later McCallon confessed, "I was all stunned and didn't know what to say."

Shortly after 9:00 A.M. New York time, George Putnam received a transatlantic call from Londonderry in the north of Ireland. It was his wife.

"I DID IT," she shouted.

Reports varied on the time it took her to make this flight that turned her into a real pilot in her own eyes and placed her in the American pantheon of heroes, which till then was exclusively male: Charles A. Lindbergh, Babe Ruth, and Jack Dempsey, among others.

The *New York Times* stated she had flown 14 hours, 56 minutes. She said the trip took 13:30. Some sources today say her time was 15:18. Whatever her time, she had clearly broken a 16:15 record set in 1919. Not only was Amelia Earhart the first woman to wing her way alone over the Atlantic, but she did it in record time. She was also the first woman to fly across it twice.

THE ACROBATS
Dorothy Aldis

Flying high on silver bars
Ladies spangled like the sun
Turn just so, and then let go—
And catch another one!
And smile when they come down, and wave,
And are not proud of being brave.

PEOPLE WHO MUST
Carl Sandburg

I painted on the roof of a skyscraper.
I painted a long while and called it a day's work.
The people on a corner swarmed and the traffic cop's
   whistle never let up all afternoon.
They were the same as bugs, many bugs on their way—
Those people on the go or at a standstill;
And the traffic cop a spot of blue, a splinter of brass,
Where the black tides ran around him
And he kept the street. I painted a long while
And called it a day's work.

illustrated by G. Brian Karas

78

FIREMAN'S SONG

1845

Behold the noble Fireman,
All dressed in red and black,
He climbs the tilted ladder
With a rope upon his back.
An axe he carries by his side,
A helmet on his head,
He goes to fight the fire,
Most powerful and dread.
He is our unsung hero,
This man of brawn and might,
And to watch him fight a fire
Is a great and wondrous sight.

FINE ART
RISKS AND CONSEQUENCES

Saint George Killing the Dragon. c. 1438. Bernardo Martorell.

Margaret Bourke-White
atop the Chrysler Building.
1931–1933. Probably taken by
Oscar Graubner.

Photograph. Estate of Margaret
Bourke-White/*Life* magazine

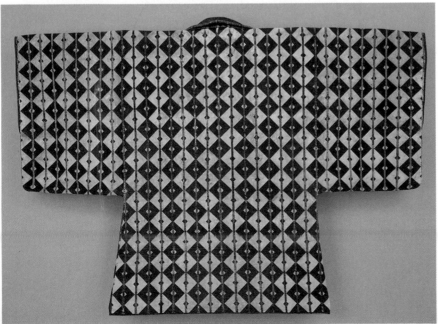

Daimyo's
firefighting
jacket. c. 1800.
Japanese.

Deerskin with
paste-resist patterns
and smoke-induced
color. Gift of Virginia
and Bagley Wright,
The Seattle Art
Museum. 89.93.
Photo: Paul Macapia

JASON AND THE GOLDEN FLEECE

C. J. Naden

illustrated by Robert Baxter

G reat adventure stories are filled with danger and excitement, with fierce battles and impossible tasks. There are dreadful monsters and brave heroes too. The story of Jason and his search for the Golden Fleece has all of these things, and more. Some people say it is the greatest adventure story of all time.

The story begins when Jason was a little boy. His father was a King, but a weak ruler. He was so weak that one day the King's nephew, Pelias, took over the throne. Pelias was an evil man and he was powerful. Jason's father was afraid that the new King might harm his son. So Jason was sent far from the kingdom to grow up in safety.

The people of the kingdom did not like their new ruler. Pelias knew that, and he trusted no one. But a prophet told him not to worry about danger from his own people. Instead, the King was warned of a stranger who would wear only one sandal. This man would cause the King's death. Pelias was very frightened when he heard the warning.

One day, many years after Pelias took the throne, a stranger walked into the marketplace. Everyone stopped to stare at him. He was tall and handsome, well dressed and well spoken. But he wore only one sandal. His bare foot was brown and dusty. It looked as though he had lost the shoe a long time ago and had walked many miles.

When Pelias heard about the stranger, he was very frightened. He remembered the words of the prophet long ago. The King drove his chariot quickly to the marketplace. The stranger was there, talking quietly to the people. "Who are you?" demanded the King. "What do you want in my land?" The stranger looked at Pelias and smiled. But the smile was not friendly.

"I am Jason," the stranger said. "I am your cousin. And I have come to take back the throne that you stole from my

father. If you do not return what is mine, I will take it from you." Jason's words struck great fear into the King's heart. For Pelias was a coward. He knew that he would not fight Jason. But he would not give up the throne either. What could he do? Then an idea came to him.

"You claim the throne, my dear cousin," said Pelias softly. "But surely a new King must first prove himself to his people. You have heard that many years ago the god Hermes sent down a magic ram. The ram's Golden Fleece is now held by the King of Colchis. But it rightfully belongs to Greece. If you can bring it back, you will also bring honor to us. Then I will gladly give up the throne."

Jason was thrilled with the idea of such a daring adventure. And Pelias was very happy because he knew that the young man would never return alive from such a journey. "I will find the Golden Fleece," Jason said to his cousin. "And I will come back to claim the throne that is mine." Pelias only smiled, for his heart was no longer afraid.

The first thing Jason did was to hire the master shipbuilder, Argus, to build the strongest ship that had ever sailed the sea. The ship was called the *Argo*. Those who sailed on it would be known as Argonauts. Great warriors came from all over the country to help Jason in his daring search for the Golden Fleece.

The ship was ready at last, and the adventure began. Jason poured wine on the ocean waves to ask the gods' blessing for a safe and successful journey. All the Argonauts knew that many dangers lay ahead. They knew that some would lose their lives. But they would find the Golden Fleece, and they would bring it back. Of that they were sure!

After many days of sailing, the Argonauts stopped to rest on an island. There they came upon an old man called Phineus. He was withered and frail, more dead than alive. They tried to give him food, but Phineus pushed them away. "I cannot eat," said the old man. "The mighty god Zeus has punished me for being too clever." The Argonauts knew that Zeus could be a jealous god.

The punishment was terrible indeed. Every time that Phineus tried to eat, horrible winged creatures called Harpies swooped down upon him. They scratched and clawed until they ripped the food from his hands and flew away. Phineus could eat nothing at all. Now he was dying.

"We can free you from this curse!" cried two of the Argonauts. They told Phineus to put out food to eat, and then they waited. In moments, the dreadful Harpies swooped down from the sky and tore at the food. But the two Argonauts fought so fiercely that the Harpies flew away. And they never returned.

"You have saved my life!" Phineus cried. He was so grateful that he told the Argonauts the secret of the Clashing Rocks. They knew that to reach Colchis they had to sail between two huge rocks in the sea. These rocks smashed against each other without warning. If their ship was caught between them, it would be smashed to bits.

"Take a dove with you," said Phineus. "Release it when you reach the Clashing Rocks. If the dove flies through unharmed, follow it quickly. Your ship will pass safely, too. But if the dove dies, you must turn back. Your ship will be broken to bits if you try to pass between the rocks."

Jason thanked the old man, and the Argonauts sailed away with a dove aboard. Soon they reached the Clashing Rocks. They watched with wide eyes as the great stones smashed into each other with deafening noise. How could they sail their ship between them? Surely they would be crushed! Each Argonaut was silent with fear. Jason released the dove, as Phineus had told him to do.

The Argonauts watched as the dove flew slowly toward the rocks. It circled lazily for a moment, and then, quickly, it glided through unharmed. "Hurry!" Jason called to his men. "Row as you have never rowed before!" The mighty *Argo* cut sharply through the waves as the men pulled at the oars. Just as they reached the Clashing Rocks, the huge stones opened and the *Argo* sailed through. They were safe.

The journey to Colchis was long and dangerous. But at last the *Argo* sailed into the harbor. They had reached the land of the Golden Fleece. The King of Colchis came down to the shore to greet them. He was very curious about these strangers and their beautiful ship. "I am Jason," said their leader. "I have come for the Golden Fleece."

The King smiled at the young man's boldness. But he had no intention of giving up the Golden Fleece. So he said, "Surely you would agree that you must earn such a valuable gift." Jason nodded. "Very well," said the King. "This task is for you alone. You must harness my two fire-breathing bulls. Then you must use them to sow a field with the teeth of a dragon."

"When you have sown the field," the King continued, "the teeth will spring up as armed warriors. You must kill each one that attacks you. Then you will have the Golden Fleece." The King smiled again, but Jason's heart grew heavy. He knew that no one, not even a warrior as brave and strong as he, could do this impossible task. The Golden Fleece seemed lost.

But luck was with Jason. Sometimes the gods and goddesses, who lived on lofty Mount Olympus, came to the aid of mortals. And Hera, Queen of all the gods, decided to help Jason because she admired his courage. She called Aphrodite, the goddess of love. Together they told Aphrodite's son, young Eros, to shoot his magic arrows into the heart of Medea. She was the daughter of the King of Colchis.

Eros shot his arrows, and Medea immediately fell in love with Jason. Because she was in love, she decided to help him. Medea was beautiful, and she was skilled in magic. She gave Jason a powerful oil to protect him in battle. Then Medea wept because she knew that she was betraying her father. But she could not help herself. "I will not forget you," Jason promised.

The next morning Jason put the magic oil over his body. With Medea and the King and the Argonauts watching, he harnessed the fire-breathing bulls and began to sow the field. As each armed warrior sprang up, Jason struck him down with one thrust of his sword. Time and again, Jason was attacked. But he slew them all. Everyone but Medea

was astonished. The King could not believe it. Jason had won the Golden Fleece.

But the King of Colchis was not ready to give up. When the Argonauts sailed away, with Medea and the Golden Fleece on board, the King sent his own ships after them. "Kill Jason!" he ordered. Once more Medea saved them. With her magic powers, she killed the King's warriors. But in so doing, she was forced to kill her own brother. Her sorrow was great.

The *Argo* sailed proudly back to Greece. With the Golden Fleece in his hand, Jason claimed the throne from Pelias. But Pelias refused to give it up. He ordered all of his soldiers to protect him from Jason. But Medea had a plan. This time she used a cunning trick of magic.

First, Medea went to see the daughters of Pelias. "I have magic powers," she told them. "I can make your aging father young and strong again." Medea cut up an old ram and boiled it in water. Then she said some magic words. The ram sprang up, young and healthy once more. The daughters of Pelias were astounded. What a marvelous gift they could give to their father.

Believing in Medea's magic, the daughters of Pelias killed him. And they waited for Medea to say the magic words that would make Pelias young and healthy again. But, of course, Medea did not say the words. Pelias was dead. He would remain dead. And Jason was now the King.

TWO TICKETS
TO FREEDOM

Florence B. Freedman

illustrated by Robert Roth

Among the many slaves in Georgia in 1848 were a young couple named William and Ellen Craft. Ellen was a maid and William a skilled cabinetmaker. Their lives were not as harsh as those of many other slaves, but the desire to be free never left them. However, escaping would be difficult!

William had been saving money for tickets to escape. He had a plan for himself and Ellen, who was light-skinned enough to pass for white. Ellen would dress up as an injured man, bandaging her face to further disguise the fact that she was a woman, and bandaging her right arm and hand to prevent anyone from asking her to write. She would then travel with William as her slave.

Their journey would include a train ride to Fredericksburg, Virginia, followed by a boat trip to Washington, D.C., and finally a train ride to Philadelphia, the first stop on the Underground Railroad.

By the time they left the train in Fredericksburg and boarded a ship for Washington, D.C., William and Ellen felt sure they were safe. They were unaware that the most difficult part of their daring escape was just around the corner. Would they ever make it to Philadelphia?

In a few minutes, the ship landed at Washington, and there William and Ellen took a carriage to the train for Baltimore, the last slave port they were to see. They had left their cottage on Wednesday morning, the 21st of December. It was Christmas Eve, December 24, 1848, when they arrived in Baltimore.

William and Ellen were more tense than ever. They were so near their goal . . . yet they knew that officials in Baltimore were particularly watchful to prevent slaves from escaping across the border to Pennsylvania and freedom.

William settled his "master" in a first-class carriage on the train and went to the car in which blacks traveled. Before he entered, a Yankee officer stopped him, saying sternly, "Where are you going, boy?"

"Philadelphia, sir," William replied humbly.

"What are you going there for?" asked the officer.

"I am traveling with my master who is in another carriage, sir."

"I think you had better get him out, and be quick about
it, because the train will soon be starting," the officer
ordered. "It is against the rules to let any man take a slave
past here unless he can satisfy them in the office that he has
a right to take him along." The officer moved on, leaving
William on the platform.

William's heart was beating furiously. To have come so
far—and now this! How would Ellen be able to prove ownership? He consoled himself with the thought that God,

who had been so good as to allow them to come this far, would not let them be turned aside now.

William hastened into the car to tell his master the bad news. "Mr. Johnson," seated comfortably in the railroad car, smiled at him. They were so near their destination.

"How are you feeling, sir?" asked William.

"Much better," answered his "master." "Thank God we are getting on so nicely."

"Not so nicely, sir, I am sorry to say," William said. "You must leave the train and convince the officials that I am your slave."

"Mr. Johnson" shuddered.

"Good heavens!" he whispered. "Is it possible that we will be sent back into slavery?"

They were silent for a few despairing moments. Then they left the train and made their way to the office.

Ellen summoned her last bit of courage.

"Do you wish to see me, sir?" "Mr. Johnson" asked the man who appeared to be the chief officer.

"Yes," he answered. "It is against our rules, sir, to allow any person to take a slave out of Baltimore into Philadelphia unless he can satisfy us that he has a right to take him along."

"Why is that?" asked "Mr. Johnson" innocently.

"Because, sir," the officer answered in a voice and manner that almost chilled the blood of the fugitives, "if we should allow any gentleman to take a slave past here into Philadelphia, and should the gentleman with whom the slave was traveling turn out to be not his rightful owner, and if the real owner should prove that his slave escaped on our railroad, we should have to pay for him."

This conversation attracted the attention of a large number of curious passengers. They seemed sympathetic to "Mr. Johnson," because he was so obviously ill.

Seeing the sympathy of the other passengers, the officer asked, more politely, "Do you know someone in Baltimore who might vouch for you and assure us that you have a right to take this slave into Pennsylvania?"

"No, I do not," asserted "Mr. Johnson" regretfully. He then added more forcefully, "I bought tickets in Charleston to pass us through to Philadelphia, and you have no right to detain us here!"

The officer was firm. "Right or wrong, I shan't let you go."

William and Ellen looked at each other, but did not dare to say a word for fear they would give themselves away. They knew that, if the officer suspected them, he had the right to put them in prison. When their true identity became known, they would surely be sent back into slavery, and they knew they would rather be dead. They silently prayed to be delivered from this new danger.

Just then, the conductor of the train on which they had come from Washington, came in.

"Did this gentleman and his slave come on your train?" asked the official.

"They did," answered the conductor, and left.

Suddenly the bell rang for the train to leave. The other passengers fixed their eyes upon the officer, "Mr. Johnson," and his slave, their expressions showing their interest and concern.

The officer seemed agitated. Running his fingers through his hair, he finally said, "I don't know what to do." Then looking around, he added, "I calculate it is all right. Run and tell the conductor that it will be all right to let this gentleman and his slave proceed," he told one of the clerks. "Since he is not well, it is a pity to stop him here. We will let him go."

"Mr. Johnson" thanked him and stepped out, crossing the platform as quickly as possible, with his slave close behind. William escorted his master into one of the best carriages of the train and reached his own just as the train pulled out.

It was eight o'clock on Christmas Eve, just eight days after William had first thought of their plan. In the four days before they left Macon, he and Ellen had both been working; they had seen each other only at night, when they talked over each detail of their plan. They had had hardly any sleep for the four days of planning and the four days of the journey. Now that the last hurdle was passed, William realized how terribly tired he was. Knowing that they would be in Philadelphia in the morning, and that there were no important stations between Baltimore and Philadelphia, William relaxed his guard, and fell asleep. It proved to be the wrong time for sleeping.

When the train reached Havre-de-Grace, all the first-class passengers were told to get off the train and onto a ferryboat, to be ferried across the Susquehanna River to take the train again on the opposite side. This was to spare the passengers the jolting of rolling the cars onto the boat. The baggage cars, however, were rolled on the boat to be taken off on the other side. The sleeping William was near the baggage car, so they did not wake him.

When Ellen left the railroad carriage to get on the ferryboat, it was cold and dark and rainy. She was alone, without William, for the first time on the journey. She was frightened and confused.

"Have you seen my boy?" "Mr. Johnson" asked the conductor.

The conductor, who may well have been an abolitionist, thought he would tease this Southern slaveowner.

"No, I haven't seen anything of him for some time; no doubt he has run away and has reached Philadelphia long before now. He is probably a free man by now, sir."

"Mr. Johnson" knew better. "Please try to find him," he asked the conductor.

"I am no slave hunter," the conductor indignantly replied. "As far as I am concerned, everybody must look after his own slaves." With that, he strode away.

Ellen was frightened. She feared that William had been kidnaped into slavery, or perhaps killed on the train. She was in a predicament for another reason. She had no money at all. Although Ellen had been carrying the money up to then, she had given it all to William the night before after hearing that there were pickpockets in Philadelphia who preyed on travelers. A pickpocket would not think of a slave as a likely victim.

Ellen did have the tickets, however. Frightened and confused though she was, she realized that there was no use in her staying there at Havre-de-Grace. She must board the ferry and complete her journey, hoping and praying that she and William would find each other again in freedom.

The ferry ride over, the passengers went back on the train. After the train was well on its way to Philadelphia, the guard came to the car where William was sleeping and gave him a violent shake, saying, "Boy, wake up!"

William started, not knowing for a moment where he was.

"Your master is scared half to death about you," the guard continued. It was William's turn to be scared. He was sure that Ellen had been found out.

"What is the matter?" William managed to ask.

"Your master thinks you have run away from him," the guard explained.

Knowing that Ellen would never think any such thing, William felt reassured and went to his "master" immediately.

After talking with "Mr. Johnson" for a few minutes, William returned to his place, where the guard was talking with the conductor.

"What did your master want, boy?" asked the guard.

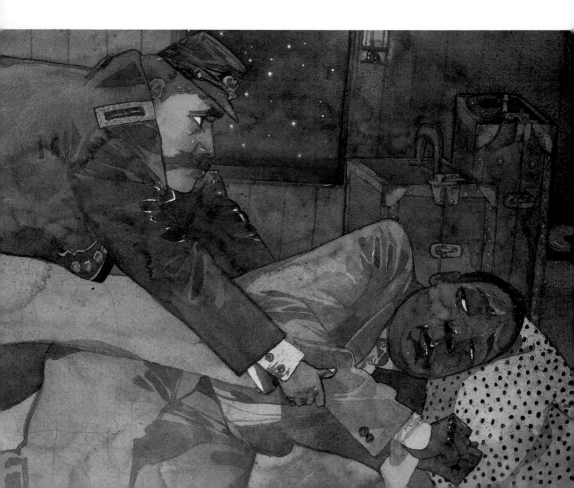

"He just wanted to know what had become of me."

"No," said the guard. "That's not it. He thought you had taken leave for parts unknown. I never saw a man so badly scared about losing his slave in my life. Now," continued the guard, "let me give you a little friendly advice. When you get to Philadelphia, run away and leave that cripple, and have your liberty."

"No, sir," replied William. "I can't promise to do that."

"Why not?" asked the conductor, evidently much surprised. "Don't you want your liberty?"

"Yes, sir," he replied, "but I shall never run away from such a good master as I have at present."

One of the men said to the guard, "Let him alone. I guess he'll open his eyes when he gets to Philadelphia."

In spite of William's seeming lack of interest, the men gave him a good deal of information about how to run away from his master in Philadelphia, information which he appeared not to be taking to heart, but which he found useful for both of them later.

On the train, William also met a free black man, who recommended to him a boardinghouse in Philadelphia kept by an abolitionist, where he would be quite safe if he decided to run away from his master. William thanked him, but did not let him know who he and his "master" really were.

Later on in the night, William heard a fearful whistling of the steam engine; he looked out the window and saw many flickering lights. A passenger in the next car also stuck his head out the window and called to his companion,

"Wake up! We are in Philadelphia." The sight of the city in
the distance and the words he heard made William feel as
if a burden had rolled off his back; he felt really happy for
the first time in his life.

As soon as the train reached the platform, he went to get "Mr. Johnson," took their luggage, put it into a carriage, got in and drove off to the abolitionist's boardinghouse recommended to him by the free black man.

No sooner had they left the station than Ellen, who had concealed her fears and played her part with so much courage and wit throughout the journey, grasped William's hand and said, "Thank God we are safe!" She burst into tears, and wept like a child.

When they reached the boardinghouse, Ellen was so weak and faint that she could scarcely stand alone. As soon as they were shown their room, William and Ellen knelt down and thanked God for His goodness in enabling them to overcome so many dangers in escaping from slavery to freedom.

That was Sunday, December 25, Christmas Day of 1848.

Ellen was twenty-two years old, and William a few years older. They thought all their troubles were over. They were young, strong, and in love. And they were free.

Philadelphia was the first stop on the Underground Railroad for William and Ellen. Eventually, they made their way to England, where their children were born. After the Civil War, they returned to Georgia with their family and bought a large plantation. There they established the Woodville Cooperative Farm School for poor families, to which they devoted the rest of their lives.

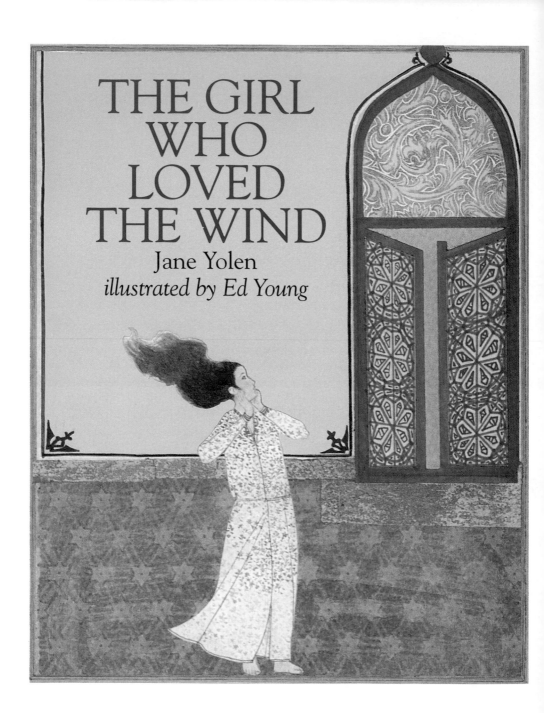

THE GIRL
WHO
LOVED
THE WIND

Jane Yolen
illustrated by Ed Young

Once many years ago in a country far to the east there lived a wealthy merchant. He was a widower and had an only daughter named Danina. She was dainty and beautiful, and he loved her more than he loved all of his treasures.

Because Danina was his only child, the merchant wanted to keep her from anything that might hurt or harm her in any way, and so he decided to shut her away from the world.

When Danina was still an infant, her father brought her to a great house which he had built on the shore of the sea. On three sides of the house rose three huge walls. And on the fourth side was the sea itself.

In this lovely, lonely place Danina grew up knowing everything that was in her father's heart but nothing of the world.

In her garden grew every kind of fair fruit and flower, for so her father willed it. And on her table was every kind of fresh fish and fowl, for so her father ordered. In her room were the finest furnishings. Gaily colored books and happy music, light dancing and bright paintings, filled her days. And the servants were instructed always to smile, never to say no, and to be cheerful all through the year. So her father wished it and so it was done. And for many years, nothing sad touched Danina in any way.

Yet one spring day, as Danina stood by her window gazing at the sea, a breeze blew salt across the waves. It whipped her hair about her face. It blew in the corners of her room. And as it moved, it whistled a haunting little tune.

Danina had never heard such a thing before. It was sad, but it was beautiful. It intrigued her. It beguiled her. It caused her to sigh and clasp her hands.

"Who are you?" asked Danina.

And the wind answered:

> *Who am I?*
> *I call myself the wind.*
> *I slap at ships and sparrows.*
> *I sough through broken windows.*
> *I shepherd snow and sandstorms.*
> *I am not always kind.*

"How peculiar," said Danina. "Here you merely rustle the trees and play with the leaves and calm the birds in their nests."

"*I am not always kind,*" said the wind again.

"Everyone here is always kind. Everyone here is always happy."

"*Nothing is always,*" said the wind.

"My life is always," said Danina. "Always happy."

"*But life is not always happy,*" said the wind.

"Mine is," said Danina.

"*How sad,*" whispered the wind from a corner.

"What do you mean?" asked Danina. But the wind only whirled through the window carrying one of her silken scarves, and before she could speak again, he had blown out to sea.

Days went by, happy days. Yet sometimes in her room, Danina would try to sing the wind's song. She could not quite remember the words or recall the tune, but its strangeness haunted her.

Finally, one morning, she asked her father: "Why isn't life always happy?"

"Life *is* always happy," replied her father.

"That's what I told him," said Danina.

"Told who?" asked her father. He was suddenly frightened, frightened that someone would take his daughter away.

"The wind," said Danina.

"The wind does not talk," said her father.

"He called himself the wind," she replied.

But her father did not understand. And so when a passing fisherman found Danina's scarf far out at sea and returned it to the merchant's house, he was rewarded with a beating, for the merchant suspected that the fisherman was the one who called himself the wind.

Then one summer day, weeks later, when the sun was reflected in the petals of the flowers, Danina strolled in her garden. Suddenly the wind leaped over the high wall and pushed and pulled at the tops of the trees. He sang his strange song, and Danina clasped her hands and sighed.

"Who are you?" she whispered.

"*Who am I?*" said the wind, and he sang:

> *Who am I?*
> *I call myself the wind.*
> *I've worked the sails of windmills.*
> *I've whirled the sand in deserts.*
> *I've wrecked ten thousand galleons.*
> *I am not always kind.*

"I knew it was you," said Danina. "But no one believed me."

And the wind danced around the garden and made the flowers bow.

He caressed the birds in the trees and played gently with the feathers on their wings.

"You say you are not always kind," said Danina. "You say you have done many unkind things. But all I see is that you are gentle and good."

"*But not always,*" reminded the wind. "*Nothing is always.*"

"Is it sad then beyond the wall?"

"Sometimes sad and sometimes happy," said the wind.

"But different each day?" said Danina.

"Very different."

"How strange," Danina said. "Here things are always the same. Always beautiful. Happy. Good."

"How sad," said the wind. "How dull." And he leaped over the wall and blew out into the world.

"Come back," shouted Danina, rushing to the wall. But her voice was lost against the stones.

Just then her father came into the garden. He saw his daughter standing by the wall and crying to the top. He ran over to her. "Who are you calling? Who has been here?" he demanded.

"The wind," said Danina, her eyes bright with memory. "He sang me his song."

"The wind does not sing," said her father. "Only men and birds sing."

"This was no bird," said his daughter.

"Then," thought her father, "it must have been a man." And he resolved to keep Danina from the garden.

Locked out of her garden, Danina began to wander up and down the long corridors of the house, and what once had seemed like a palace to her began to feel like a prison. Everything seemed false. The happy smiles of the servants she saw as smiles of pity for her ignorance. The gay dancing seemed to hide broken hearts. The bright paintings hid sad thoughts. And soon Danina found herself thinking of the wind at every moment, humming his song to the walls. His song about the world—sometimes happy, sometimes sad, but always full of change and challenge.

Her father, who was not cruel but merely foolish, could not keep her locked up completely. Once a day, for an hour, he allowed Danina to walk along the beach. But three maidservants walked before her. Three manservants walked behind. And the merchant himself watched from a covered chair.

One chilly day in the fall, when the tops of the waves rolled in white to the shore, Danina strolled on the beach. She pulled her cape around her for warmth. And the three maidservants before her and the three manservants behind shivered in the cold. Her father in his covered chair pulled his blanket to his chin and stared out to sea. He was cold and unhappy, but he was more afraid to leave Danina alone.

Suddenly the wind blew across the caps of the waves, tossing foam into the air.

Danina turned to welcome him, stretching out her arms. The cape billowed behind her like the wings of a giant bird.

"Who are you?" thundered Danina's father, jumping out of his chair.

The wind spun around Danina and sang:

Who am I?
I call myself the wind.
I am not always happy.
I am not always kind.

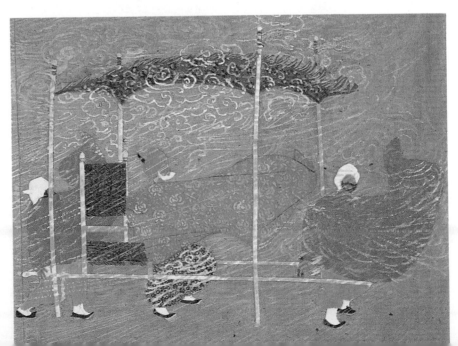

"Nonsense," roared Danina's father. "Everyone here is always happy and kind. I shall arrest you for trespassing." And he shouted, "GUARDS!"

But before the guards could come, Danina had spread her cape on the water. Then she stepped onto it, raised one corner, and waved good-bye to her father. The blowing wind filled the cape's corner like the sail of a ship.

And before Danina's father had time to call out, before he had time for one word of repentance, she was gone. And the last thing he saw was the billowing cape as Danina and the wind sailed far to the west into the ever-changing world.

MEET JANE YOLEN, AUTHOR

Jane Yolen has written numerous books for children of all ages. She is often asked for advice on becoming a writer. "I have two pieces of advice for young people interested in writing: read and write. Read and read and read. It's the only way you will discover what great stories have been told, and what stories you want to tell better. Write every day because writing is like a muscle that needs to be flexed. I don't physically exercise as much as I should, but I do exercise my writing every day."

On the writing process Yolen explains: "I would say that each book I ever worked on has had at least three or four major revisions. I take things out, throw them away, and reshape. That comes from being a poet. I read everything aloud and when you read aloud you hear it again, the way you would a poem." Yolen also keeps an idea file with anything that comes along. It is from this file that she gets many of her new story ideas.

MEET ED YOUNG, ILLUSTRATOR

Ed Young was born in China and grew up in Shanghai. He became an illustrator of children's books because he enjoyed "telling stories through pictures." Among his best-known works are Yeh Shen (the Chinese version of Cinderella), Lon Po Po, The Emperor and the Kite, Cats Are Cats, and Cricket Boy.

Young's pictures in The Girl Who Loved the Wind are a combination of watercolors and collage. He developed the technique specifically for this book. He wanted the pictures to look like Persian paintings.

Young has a deep interest in tai chi chuan, a form of "moving meditation," which he learned from an old Chinese master. He says that it greatly influences the way he thinks and works.

BIBLIOGRAPHY

The Enchanted Tapestry
by Robert D. San Souci.
Li Ju, a Chinese boy, begins a
dangerous search for his mother's
handmade tapestry, held by the
fairies of Sun Mountain.

*Escape from Slavery: Five Journeys
to Freedom* by Doreen Rappaport.
This book contains five true stories
of daring escapes to freedom by
slaves.

Flight by Robert Burleigh.
Read about the incredible
accomplishments of an early
aviator, Charles Lindbergh.

Millie Cooper, Take a Chance
by Charlotte Herman.
After trying two different ways to
win a bicycle and forcing herself to
read a poem in front of her third-
grade class, Millie learns about the
rewards of taking chances.

Rescue! True Stories of Heroism
by L. B. Taylor, Jr.
The Carnegie Hero Fund
Commission was founded to honor
those who risk their lives to save
others. This book tells about the
history of the organization and
gives examples of amazing
heroic deeds.

Risk N' Roses by Jan Slepian.
Skip and her friends get into
a lot of trouble when they accept a
neighbor girl's dares!

Shiloh by Phyllis Reynolds Naylor.
Marty hides a mistreated dog from
his parents and from the neighbor
who owns it.

Stone Fox by John Reynolds
Gardiner. Willy tries to win money
to save his grandfather's farm by
entering a dogsled race. Will he
win, or will last year's winner beat
him again?

LEMONADE STAND

Myra Cohn Livingston
illustrated by Bob Barner

Every summer
under the shade
we fix up a stand
to sell lemonade.

A stack of cups,
a pitcher of ice,
a shirtboard sign
to tell the price.

A dime for the big,
A nickel for small.
The nickel cup's short.
The dime cup's tall.

Plenty of sugar
to make it sweet,
and sometimes cookies
for us to eat.

But when the sun
moves into the shade
it gets too hot
to sell lemonade.

Nobody stops
so we put things away
and drink what's left
and start to play.

PRICE
BIG 10¢
Small 5¢

LEMONADE

EDDIE, INCORPORATED

Phyllis Reynolds Naylor
illustrated by Laura Cornell

The South End Middle School was composed of sixth, seventh, and eighth graders instead of the usual junior high arrangement. Every noon, the students had an hour off for something called activity period. During this time they ate their lunch and afterwards they could walk around, talk with teachers, use the library, and go outside and throw frisbees.

Eddie called a business conference during activity period. While their other sixth-grade friends were shooting baskets over on the concrete, Eddie, Dink, and Elizabeth sat on the wall at the driveway entrance and had a meeting.

It was understood from the beginning that they were partners. They would all three be bosses, so nobody could tell them what to do.

"We've got to have advertising," said Eddie.

Elizabeth lifted her face toward the warm May sun and closed her eyes for a moment. She wore huge, round, blue-tinted glasses, and her hair was pulled up in a large topknot.

"What we need," she said, "is to rent a plane that would fly all over Detroit trailing a banner that said, 'Anselmino's Aluminum Recycling Now Open for Business.'"

She even looked like an executive.

"Elizabeth can do advertising," said Eddie, and knew she'd think of something, even without the plane. "We also need someone in charge of supply—to find out where the cans are and go after them."

"I could use Dad's garbage can carrier and go around collecting," Dink said. He was wearing a tee-shirt with Godzilla on the front. He didn't look like an executive, but he did look as though he could walk over half of Detroit pushing a one-hundred pound load.

"You've got it," said Eddie. "Vice-president in charge of supply."

"Hey, Eddie," Billy Watson called. "Let's shoot a few baskets."

"Not now," said Eddie. "We've got business."

Eddie himself was in charge of the factory, which was half the Anselminos' basement. He set up a card table with a clock and a pen and a notebook on it. He propped up a long piece of rain gutter under the basement window as a chute, a packing box to catch the cans, a tub to rinse them in, a hair dryer to dry them, a sledge hammer to flatten them, and a box of leaf bags to bind them up in five-pound bundles.

All week long Elizabeth went about the neighborhood tacking handmade posters on telephone poles. The announcement read:

Tired of litter?
Sick of junk?
ANSELMINO'S ALUMINUM
RECYCLING COMPANY
needs your old cans

And then it listed Eddie's address and phone number.

Dink had painted a big OPEN sign on the back of a dart board to set up outside the house. The Anselmino Aluminum Recycling Company would begin its first day of business on Saturday, May 17, at nine o'clock.

"I'll be here at eight-thirty, in case there's a line," Elizabeth said to Eddie on Friday.

"And we ought to put in a night deposit box so people will have some place to put their cans after we're closed,"

Dink suggested. He said he would make one and bring it with him on Saturday.

Even Eddie's brother Joseph was interested in the company.

"How much can you get for aluminum cans, Eddie?" he asked at dinner.

"Seventeen cents a pound."

Joseph figured it out on the calculator he had wedged between his leg and the seat of his chair. "Only five hundred and eighty-eight pounds and you'll have a hundred dollars," he said, and went on to figure the interest.

"What are you going to do with the profits?" Eddie's other brother, Roger, asked Eddie. "Have you thought of investing it somewhere? The bank gives five and one half percent."

Actually, Eddie had been thinking of putting it in the back of his top dresser drawer under the extra shoelaces, but he said he'd consider investing.

"And what about Dink and Elizabeth?" Mr. Anselmino asked. "Are you putting them on salary, or do they share the profits?"

Eddie wasn't sure.

"If they're on salary," his father said, "that means you pay them a certain amount each week regardless of how much the company takes in. If the company loses money, you'll have to pay them out of your allowance or something. But if the company makes money, they still get only their salary and you get all the rest."

It wasn't difficult to decide that one. Eddie, Dink, and Elizabeth were a team. It would be share and share alike. Even if they made a hundred dollars the first day, they'd split it three ways.

"We're sharing the profits," he said, and realized he was beginning to sound like Roger. It was a good feeling, especially when he understood what he was talking about.

"Who's going to pay for the leaf bags you took out of the tool shed?" asked Mrs. Anselmino.

"We'll take it out of our earnings," Eddie told her. They hadn't even opened for business and already they were sixty-three cents in debt.

He woke at five the next morning and looked out the window to see if a line was forming yet. The street was still dark and empty. He knew he wouldn't sleep anymore, so he got up, dressed, and went out on the porch to wait.

The paper boy came by, followed by his dog. The mutt was holding something in his mouth that looked familiar. Eddie went down the steps and took it away from him. It was one of the advertisements for the Anselmino Aluminum Recycling Company.

"Hey, where'd he get this?" Eddie called after the boy.

The paper boy shrugged. "I don't know. It was blowing around on the street back there."

Eddie went down to the corner. The poster had been ripped off the telephone pole. There was still a piece of it left. He walked over to the next street. That poster was there, but someone had drawn two tanks on it, having a

war, with smoke and bombs all over the words. At the next telephone pole, someone had crossed out Eddie's telephone number and scribbled in the number for the fire department instead.

He went back home and sat on the steps. This neighborhood didn't have too many old cans; it had too many rotten children. Anselmino's Children Recycling Company, that's what it ought to be. They ought to go around collecting bratty kids in Dink's garbage cart, weigh them in, tie them in sacks, and send them off to Siberia.

Mrs. Anselmino found Eddie still on the porch at seven o'clock and made him come in for breakfast. She put a plate of scrambled eggs before him and a sausage and an English muffin and then, on the spur of the moment, she poured him a half cup of coffee and filled the cup up with cream.

"Now," she said, "you're ready for business."

He was beginning to feel good again.

Dink and Elizabeth arrived at eight-thirty. Dink had brought a night-deposit box made out of an ice cream container. On the curb at the end of the driveway he placed the dart board sign saying, OPEN.

At five minutes till nine, they took their places —Dink outside the basement window, Elizabeth at the bottom of the chute, and Eddie at the card table desk.

On the top of the first page of his notebook, Eddie wrote, "The Anselmino Aluminum Recycling Company" and, as an afterthought, added, "Incorporated," though he wasn't sure what it meant.

Underneath, he made six vertical columns with a ruler. At the top of the first column he wrote, "Date." At the top of the second, he wrote "Number of cans." At the top of the third, "Number of pounds." At the fourth, "Income," the fifth, "Expenses," and at the top of the final column he wrote "Profit." Then, after a moment, he added, ". . . or Loss."

Nine o'clock came, nine-fifteen, and at twenty after, Dink yelled, "Somebody's coming!"

There were footsteps on the driveway outside, and the sound of the mailman's voice. He wanted to know where the aluminum deposit was, and Dink directed him to the open window.

The sleeve of a blue uniform came through the window and deposited one empty iced tea can in the rain gutter.

Clunk-ity . . . Clunk-ity . . . thunk.

It was a very lonely sound. The iced tea can lay all by itself in the bottom of the packing box, and the blue uniform disappeared.

Elizabeth picked up the can and dropped it in the water in the wash tub, placed it under the hair dryer for a minute, and then flattened it with the sledge hammer.

"One," she said, as she set it over against the wall.

Eddie made a mark in the second column of his notebook beside May 17.

About ten o'clock, Mr. Clemmons came over with an armload of cans he had picked up in the alley. He dropped them down the chute one after another: *clunkity, clunkity, thumpity, bang, thud*. It was a beautiful noise.

"Hey, thanks a lot!" said Dink outside the window.

Now it was more like a factory. Elizabeth had barely taken all the cans out of the packing box when Dink's mother came around to the window and deposited a few cola cans and seven ginger ales. There were cans in the packing case at the bottom of the chute, cans floating about in the wash tub, cans under the hair dryer, and cans waiting to be smashed.

"This is more like it," said Eddie.

Things slowed a little over the lunch hour. Mrs. Anselmino brought down some salami sandwiches, and they took turns eating and standing out on the driveway to direct people to the deposit window.

Billy Watson and some boys from the South End Middle School rode over on their bikes, stuck their heads in the window and yelled crazy things. One of them rolled a rock down the chute. But after they went away, Elizabeth's father arrived with two grocery sacks full of cans.

"Way to go!" whooped Dink from outside as he poured the cans down the rain gutter.

Eddie and Elizabeth were working as fast as they could.

About three o'clock the hair dryer began to smell funny, and Eddie decided that maybe it needed a rest, so they finished drying the cans with a towel.

At four, old Mrs. Harris came by pulling a little wagon. It was piled high with cans, and she stooped down outside the window and began dropping them one at a time down the chute.

Eddie and Elizabeth stared. There were baked beans cans and creamed corn cans and scalloped potato cans and about twenty fruit cocktail. Only one of the cans was aluminum; the rest were tin, and the baked bean can still had a frankfurter in the bottom.

"Why didn't you stop her, Dink?" Elizabeth called up after the woman had left.

"I didn't have the heart," he said. "She pulled that wagon four blocks, so I just thanked her, and she said there were more cans where those came from."

At five o'clock, Eddie took the OPEN sign and put it behind the house. He closed the basement window and put the night deposit box in front of it. Then he and Dink and

Elizabeth went back to the basement to tally up the day's profits.

There were one-hundred and thirty-six cans. Eddie brought down the bathroom scale to see how many pounds that would be. They began putting the flattened cans on the scales one at a time.

The marker barely moved. Three cans . . . four cans . . .

"Maybe the scale is broken," said Elizabeth.

Around ten cans, they could tell that the marker had moved halfway between zero and one. It took twenty-one cans to make a pound.

Carefully they divided the cans into little heaps of twenty-one each. Six piles of cans with ten left over. Six pounds of cans at seventeen cents a pound.

Eddie went to his desk and figured it out. One dollar and two cents. He entered it under "income." Then he remembered the sixty-three cents they owed for the leaf bags and put that in the column marked "expenses." One dollar and two cents minus sixty-three cents left a profit of thirty-nine cents. And thirty-nine cents divided between Eddie, Dink, and Elizabeth was thirteen cents apiece.

"At least you didn't go in the hole," Mr. Anselmino said at dinner that evening.

"And people know where to bring the cans now," said Roger.

"And he paid off his debt to me the very first day," said Mrs. Anselmino.

Joseph had not brought his pocket calculator to the table that evening, but Eddie could tell, by the way he pressed his fingers against the table top one at a time, that he was figuring something out in his head. "Thirteen cents a day, six days a week, fifty-two times a year, at five and a half percent . . ." he was saying to himself.

But Eddie wasn't interested in what he could make if the Anselmino Aluminum Recycling Company lasted a year. He was wondering if it would last a month. Eight hours a day for only thirteen cents was just a little more than one-and-a-half cents an hour, which meant he'd have to work a day and then some just to afford a stamp to mail his income tax. Bosses had more problems than anybody.

MEET PHYLLIS REYNOLDS NAYLOR, AUTHOR

Phyllis Reynolds Naylor has written countless books for all ages. "There is a part of me in every book I write. It may simply be a place I have been or someone I have known or something that has happened to me all mixed up with things I just imagine. Some books take a great deal of research—my stories of a Seminole Indian boy, a coal miner's family in West Virginia, or a girl growing up during the Depression. Others are mostly fun and are written off the top of my head. Through my books I can be many different people, living many different places and doing all kinds of interesting things. I can take a real problem I may be experiencing and work it out on paper." Naylor says many of her story ideas come from simply wondering "what if."

GREGG NEVAREZ, YOUNG TYCOON

from THE YOUNG TYCOONS
by Gloria D. Miklowitz
and Madeleine Yates
illustrated by Marie DeJohn

Gregg Nevarez's face lit up when his friend suggested, "Let's go into the cleaning business! All you do is push dust around, vacuum, and you're done. People are making thirty dollars an hour doing that!"

The more Gregg thought about it, the more hopeful he felt. Earning that much in an hour seemed too good to be true.

During high school he had worked in the usual teenage jobs: as a gas-station attendant, box-boy at a grocery store, painter and carpenter's helper, protein-powder salesperson, and finally, driveway black-topper. Now it was time to settle down to work that offered a future.

He didn't want to go to college. He'd been only a so-so student in high school. But he did want to work and make money.

As a Chicano, a Mexican–American, he felt he was at a disadvantage. Chicanos could go only so far. His father, an aircraft worker, had achieved more than most. Gregg lived in a Caucasian neighborhood that was free of gang warfare. Both his parents worked hard to give their children a better life, and Gregg appreciated this deeply. Much of his drive to succeed came from the intense desire to repay his parents by achieving as much as he could.

Yet, from his earliest years, he realized that there were important achievement differences between Chicanos and Caucasians. He felt limitations were set, his life script written, the day he was born a Chicano. He'd be lucky to do as well as his father. That was the way it was, and the way it always would be. Still, he dreamed.

When he talked of going into the cleaning business with his friend, he heard, "You can't make money without money." "How can you do well when you barely made it through high school?" "Clean offices? Ha! You haven't cleaned your own room in a month!"

Still he was determined to try. Who would lend him the $125 he needed to get started? Not his parents. Though

they were loving and supportive, it was too hard for them to save money to risk it on a "harebrained scheme." Instead, Gregg asked a friend, Stephanie Martz. She believed in him and loaned him the money from her savings, without telling her parents. There was only a verbal promise to repay.

Most of that loan was spent for advertising. Gregg had cards and fliers printed announcing the establishment of the West Coast Office Cleaning Service as a business. He bought advertising space in a local newspaper.

When the first calls for estimates came in, Gregg and his partner were delighted. But what should they charge? "I knew that a lot of professional services charged $25 an hour, so I figured I'd charge $10 an hour." To get an idea of how long it would take to clean a typical office, he timed cleaning his own bedroom. Less than an hour. Gregg and his partner settled on $10 an office for their combined time.

They borrowed Mrs. Nevarez's vacuum cleaner for their first jobs, as well as scouring powder, glass cleaner, some sponges, a toilet brush, and some plastic garbage bags. They took rags from home.

Inexperienced as they were, it was natural that problems would arise. Clients phoned frequently, complaining. They had forgotten to lock up or scratched something or didn't clean something. Gregg's partner couldn't take the criticism, but Gregg cheerfully went back to correct any problems. He also discovered that a little psychology went a long way. When a client called to complain, he'd say, "I'm sorry if we missed that, Mrs. X. No problem. We'll take care of it right away. We want to do things right. You're a busy person and if you're taking time to call, then there must be a good reason."

Frequently, Gregg's agreeable attitude won over the caller. By the end of the call, the client often told Gregg not to bother. "Just be sure you do it the next time you come."

In two months, Gregg and his partner were earning about $1,400 a month, but the partner wanted out. "I hate dealing with complaints. I don't like bidding on jobs or doing the work. You can have the business," he said.

Soon afterward, a church in Redondo Beach, California, gave him work. He was to clean the auditorium, bathrooms, halls, offices, and classrooms for $750 a month. A very nice account! Gregg hired a helper and paid him $3.50 an hour.

Money came in and was spent, but Gregg couldn't keep track of it. He called a relative, an aunt who was an accountant with a bookkeeping service. "Would you do my books?" he asked.

"Sure," she said, "if you'll clean my office." Swapping services worked well, and Gregg thought he was probably getting the better deal.

Three months after high school graduation, the West Coast Office Cleaning Service became official. Although the business grew each month after that, by the spring of 1979, Gregg was beginning to feel depressed. His friends were in college, working toward professions or careers. He felt he'd been left behind, that what he was doing didn't really count. He often felt edgy. When a client complained, he began talking back instead of being tactful. "If you don't like it, get someone else!" He was losing accounts and, for no reason, was also losing a great deal of weight.

One day, after an evening out with friends, he felt ill. He went to a doctor, who discovered that Gregg was severely diabetic and put him in the hospital. The diagnosis was hard to accept. He would have to change his entire lifestyle. No more sugar. No more fast-food meals at odd hours, but regular meals on schedule. He'd have to take insulin shots for the rest of his life. Until the right dosage was determined, Gregg felt like a human guinea pig. Some days he felt worse than ever.

Adjusting to his illness took all of his energy and attention for nearly four months. Business was the least of his concerns. By the time he felt well again, he had lost all of his accounts.

"Now, what will I do?" he wondered. A long time before, he had thought of becoming a Franciscan priest. Then he'd wanted to work in a halfway house in New York. Now he thought of being a police officer, but after riding along with the police one day, he changed his mind. Child-abuse cases were tough to handle, he was told, so Gregg volunteered at a child-abuse center and discovered that he couldn't cope emotionally.

"What do I do best?" he asked himself. The answer was business. He decided to go back into the cleaning service.

A twenty-six-year-old relative, Ed Melendez, who had built a very successful machine-shop business, gave him advice. He also loaned him $1,000 to get a new start. Gregg wisely invested the money in a new vacuum cleaner and advertising.

He was heavily in debt. With no medical insurance, he faced huge hospital, doctor, and drug bills. He also had payments to make on a truck he'd bought earlier. And now he owed his cousin money too. The drive to succeed became an obsession, not only to earn what he owed, but to achieve something he could be proud of.

Using the same general approach as he had before, he advertised and went from door to door, promoting his service.

Satisfied customers recommended him to others. As new work came in, he discovered new opportunities.

People no longer wanted him only to dust, vacuum, and wash windows. They asked if he could strip wax from the linoleum and rewax or clean the carpeting or paint. Gregg began *subcontracting*. His first "sub" was the vice-principal of his high school, who also ran a carpet-cleaning company.

"You give me a good price to clean carpets and every time I get a job, I'll give it to you," Gregg offered. The man gave Gregg a special price, five cents less a square foot than he charged regular clients to do the job. In turn, Gregg charged the price his client would have had to pay and took the difference. The vice-principal was willing to charge Gregg less because Gregg was the one who got the job. The vice-principal could still make a profit, though he charged less.

Today, many of Gregg's accounts are real-estate dealers. These agents often own or manage apartment houses. When people move, their old apartments must be redone quickly so they can be rented again.

Even before the rooms can be cleaned, it may be necessary to repaint, strip and rewax floors, redo acoustic ceilings, or perhaps clean or replace carpeting.

Gregg has found he can offer a valuable service besides cleaning. He puts together a property-management package. When a house, apartment, or condominium becomes vacant, he estimates how much work is needed. He knows what his subcontractors will charge—the carpet cleaner charges by the square foot, the painter, by the size of the room, and so on. He offers the owner or manager of the property a price covering all of the work. He can promise faster service than is possible if the owner has to hire the workers individually.

Gregg makes a profit by getting lower prices from his subs and charging the client the full price. Gregg may charge $1,000 or more to redo an apartment, including painting, rug cleaning, window washing, and general cleanup, but the cost to him may be only about $650. He can earn $350 for calling his subs and making sure they come in when they say they will.

This is the kind of work he'd like to do more of. While cleaning services still take twenty to thirty hours a week and are the "bread and butter" of his income, he expects the refurbishing work to grow. It could bring him yearly earnings of well over $100,000. In time, he thinks he can do all of the subcontracting work himself. He would buy the machines and hire the operators.

Between the office cleaning and apartment-refurbishing, he keeps very busy. Some months he earns over $6,000, other months, less. His cleaning work involves evenings and weekends, when offices are empty. When he is free, he bids on refurbishing apartments.

"I can afford to take chances," he says. "I don't have a wife and children to support, so I can dare. If I fail, so what. No one's hurt. I can try again. There's no shame in failing. At least I will have tried."

Late at night he sits down quietly to plan and dream. His dreams are different from those of most young people. They include more than succeeding at business and making money. He wants very much to make some impact on Chicano life. He feels Mexican-American youths have few heroes to emulate. Though he is no hero, he has achieved more than most young people of his age, and he'd like to encourage others to try, to go after their goals.

Someday, he'd like to go into politics. Then he could really work toward helping his people achieve an equal status with all Americans. At the very least, he would like someday to start a Chicano Junior Achievement group.

Gregg was asked what he would advise someone who wanted to do what he did. This is what he said, "Get as much schooling as possible. I'm sorry now that I didn't pay as much attention as I should have to math. It would be helpful in keeping my accounts.

"Give yourself a week to research whether this is for you. Call cleaning services listed in the Yellow Pages. Ask what they charge, what they do. Ask if you can go in and speak with the owner. Say, 'I know you're successful, and I wonder if you'll give me some tips. I'd like to start a business like this but don't know where to begin.' Most successful businesspeople will be flattered by this approach. They'll not consider you a threat, because they're so well established. If you're honestly interested and are willing to admit ignorance, you'll get a lot of answers.

"What to ask? Where do you buy supplies at a discount? What are the minimum basic supplies I'll need? How much money will I need? How long does it take to clean a typical office? What does the work consist of? What kind of problems am I likely to run into? What pitfalls should I avoid? How do you handle dissatisfied customers? What about building security? What kind of contracts do you use?

"Prepare questions before you go, and ask others as you listen. Ask anything you think will help you better understand what you're getting into."

DICK WHITTINGTON AND HIS CAT

retold and illustrated by Marcia Brown

Long ago in England there lived a little boy named
Dick Whittington. Dick's father and mother died
when he was very young, and as he was too small to
work, he had a hard time of it. The people in the village
were poor and could spare him little more than the parings
of potatoes and now and then a crust of bread. He ran about
the country as ragged as a colt, until one day he met a

wagoner on his way to London. "Come along with me," said the wagoner. So off they set together.

Now Dick had heard of the great city of London. It was said that the people who lived there were all fine gentlemen and ladies, that there was singing and music all day long, and that the streets were paved with gold. As for the gold, "I'd be willing to get a bushel of that," said Dick to himself.

But when Dick got to London, how sad he was to find the streets covered with dirt instead of gold! And there he was in a strange place, without food, without friends, and without money. Dick was soon so cold and hungry that he wished he were back sitting by a warm fire in a country kitchen. He sat down in a corner and cried himself to sleep.

A kind gentleman saw him there and said, "Why don't you go to work, my lad?"

"That I would," said Dick, "if I could get anything to do."

"Come along with me," said the gentleman, and he led Dick to a hayfield. There he worked hard and lived merrily until the hay was made.

Now Dick was again forlorn. He wandered back to town, fainting for want of food, and laid himself down at the door of Mr. Fitzwarren, a rich merchant.

Here the cook saw him, and being an ill-natured woman, she called out, "On your way there, lazy rogue, or would you like a scalding to make you jump?"

Just then Mr. Fitzwarren came home to dinner. When he saw the dirty, ragged boy lying in his doorway, he said to him, "What ails you, boy? You look old enough to work."

"Sir, I am a poor country lad," said Dick. "I have neither father nor mother nor any friend in the world. I would be glad to work, but I've had no food for three days." Dick then tried to get up, but he was so weak he fell down again.

"Take this lad into the house," Mr. Fitzwarren ordered his servants. "Give him meat and drink. When he is stronger he can help the cook with her dirty work."

Now Dick would have lived happily with this worthy family if he had not been bumped about by the cook.

"Look sharp there, clean the spit, empty the dripping pan, sweep the floor! Step lively or—!" And down came the ladle on the boy's shoulders. For the cook was always roasting and basting, and when the spit was still, she basted his head with a broom or anything else she could lay her hands on. When Mr. Fitzwarren's daughter, Alice, saw what was going on, she warned the cook, "Treat that boy more kindly or leave this house!"

Besides the crossness of the cook, Dick had another hardship. His bed was placed in a garret where there were so many rats and mice running over his bed he could never get to sleep.

But one day a gentleman gave Dick a penny for brushing his shoes. The next day Dick saw a girl in the street with a cat under her arm. He ran up to her. "How much do you want for that cat?" he asked.

"Oh, this cat is a good mouser," said the girl. "She will bring a great deal of money."

"But I have only a penny in the world," said Dick, "and I need a cat sadly." So the girl let him have it.

Dick hid his cat in the garret because he was afraid the cook would beat her too. He always saved part of his dinner for her, and Miss Puss wasted no time in killing or frightening away all the rats and mice. Now Dick could sleep as sound as a top.

Not long after this, Mr. Fitzwarren had a ship ready to sail. He called all his servants into the parlor and asked them what they chose to send to trade. All the servants brought something but poor Dick. Since he had neither money nor goods, he couldn't think of sending anything.

"I'll put some money down for him," offered Miss Alice, and she called Dick into the parlor.

But the merchant said, "That will not do. It must be something of his own."

"I have nothing but a cat," said Dick.

"Fetch your cat, boy," said the merchant, "and let her go!"

So Dick brought Puss and handed her over to the captain of the ship with tears in his eyes. "Now the rats and mice will keep me awake all night again," he said. All the company laughed, but Miss Alice pitied Dick and gave him some half-pence to buy another cat.

While Puss was beating the billows at sea, Dick was beaten at home by the cross cook. She used him so cruelly and made such fun of him for sending his cat to sea that the poor boy decided to run away. He packed the few things he had and set out early in the morning on All-Hallows Day. He walked as far as Halloway and sat down on a stone to rest. While he was sitting there wondering which way to go, the Bells of Bow began to ring. Dong! Dong!

They seemed to say to him:

"Turn again, Whittington,
Lord Mayor of London."

"Lord Mayor of London!" said Dick to himself. "What wouldn't I give to be Lord Mayor of London and ride in such a fine coach! I'll go back and I'll take the cuffings of the cook, if I'm to be Lord Mayor of London. So home he

went. Luckily, he got into the house and about his business before the old cook came downstairs.

Meanwhile the ship with the cat on board was long beating about at sea. The winds finally drove it on the coast of Barbary. Here lived the Moors, a people unknown to the English. They came in great numbers on board to see the sailors and the goods which the captain wanted to trade.

The captain sent some of his choicest goods to the king of the country. The king was so well pleased that he invited the captain and his officer to come to his palace, about a mile from the sea.

Here they were placed on rich carpets, flowered with gold and silver. The king and queen sat at the upper end of the room, and dinner was brought in. No sooner had the servants set down the dishes than an amazing number of rats and mice rushed in. They helped themselves from every dish, scattering pieces of meat and gravy all about.

The captain in surprise turned to the nobles and asked, "Are not these vermin offensive?"

"Oh yes," said they, "very offensive! The King would give half of his treasure to be rid of them. They not only ruin his dinner, but also attack him in his chamber, even in his bed! He has to be watched while he is sleeping for fear of them!"

The captain jumped for joy. He remembered Whittington and his cat and told the king he had a creature on board the ship that would soon destroy the mice. The king's heart heaved so high at this good news that his turban dropped off his head. "Bring this creature to me!" he cried.

"Vermin are dreadful in a court! If she will do what you say, I will load your ship with ivory, gold dust and jewels in exchange for her."

Away flew the captain to the ship, while another dinner was got ready. With Puss under his arm, he returned to the palace just in time to see the rats about to devour the second dinner. At first sight of the rats and mice the cat sprang from the captain's arms. Soon she had laid most of them dead at her feet, while the rest fled to their holes.

The king rejoiced to see his old enemies destroyed. The queen asked to see Miss Puss. When the captain presented the cat, the queen was a little afraid to touch a creature that had made such havoc among the rats and mice. Finally she stroked her and said, "Puttey, puttey, puttey," for she had not learned English. The captain put the cat on the queen's lap, where she purred and played with her majesty's hand and then sang herself to sleep.

When the king learned that Miss Puss and her kittens would keep the whole country free from rats and mice, he bargained for the whole ship's cargo. He gave ten times as much for Miss Puss as for all the rest.

When the ship was loaded, the captain and his officer took leave of their majesties. A breeze springing up, they hurried on board and set sail for England.

The sun was scarcely up one morning when Mr. Fitzwarren stole from his bed to count over the cash. He had just sat down at his desk in the counting house when somebody came tap, tap-tap at the door.

"Who's there?"

"A friend. I bring you news of the good ship Unicorn!"

The merchant bustled up in such a hurry that he forgot his gout. He opened the door.

There stood the captain and his officer with a cabinet of jewels and a bill of lading. The merchant lifted up his eyes and thanked Heaven for such a prosperous voyage. They told him about the cat and showed him the caskets of diamonds and rubies they had brought for Dick.

At that the merchant cried out:

"Go call him and tell him of his fame,
And call him Mr. Whittington by name."

Dick was scouring pots in the kitchen and did not want to come into the clean parlor. "The floor is polished, and my shoes are dirty and full of nails." But the merchant made him come in and sit down.

He took Dick by the hand and said, "Mr. Whittington, I sent for you to congratulate you upon your good fortune. The captain has sold your cat to the king of Barbary. She has brought you more riches than I am worth in the world. May you long enjoy them!"

When they showed him the caskets of jewels, Dick laid the whole at his master's feet, but Mr. Fitzwarren refused it. He offered them to his mistress and his good friend Miss Alice, but they too refused the smallest part. Dick then rewarded the captain and ship's crew for the care they had

taken of Puss, and distributed presents to all the servants, even to his old enemy, the cook.

Mr. Fitzwarren advised Mr. Whittington to send for tradesmen to dress him like a gentleman, and offered him his house until he could provide himself with a better. Now when Dick's face was washed, his hair curled, his hat cocked, and he was dressed in a rich suit of clothes, he turned out a genteel young fellow.

In a little time he dropped his sheepish behavior and soon became a sprightly companion. Miss Alice, who formerly looked on him with pity, now saw him in quite another light.

When Mr. Fitzwarren noticed how fond they were of each other, he proposed a match between them. Both parties cheerfully consented.

The Lord Mayor in his coach, Court of Aldermen, Sheriffs, company of stationers, and a number of eminent merchants attended the wedding ceremony. And afterwards all were treated to an elegant entertainment.

Whittington and his bride were called the happiest couple in England. He was chosen Sheriff and was three different times elected Lord Mayor of London. In the last year of his mayoralty Whittington entertained King Henry the Fifth and his Queen.

"Never had Prince such a subject," said Henry, and Whittington replied, "Never had subject such a King!"

MEET MARCIA BROWN, AUTHOR AND ILLUSTRATOR

*Marcia Brown feels that "books are as individual as people. I am often asked
why each of my books is apt to look different from the others. Each artist has his
own way of working. I feel about each book very differently. I try
to take a good piece of time between books in order to clear the way
for the next. Travel, storytelling, puppetry, and a constant interest
in painting, all have influenced my work."*

*Brown's interest in the story of Dick Whittington and His Cat
came from her study of the music and poetry of the Middle Ages.
She made her illustrations using linoleum cuts. When she first
imagined the story, she saw everything in gold: the summer fields,
the boy's hair, a London sunrise, and Whittington's treasure.
It became one of the two main colors for the book.*

ICE CREAM CONES:

A NEW SCOOP
from WHAT IF?
by Dian Dincin Buchman
and Seli Groves
illustrated by Barbara Bruno

In 1904 the city of St. Louis, Missouri put on one of the biggest fairs ever held anywhere.

Charles Menches was one of the many people who were there to sell refreshments to the fairgoers. He sold ice cream, and the hotter it got, the more dishes of ice cream he sold. At the end of a busy day, he always had fewer dishes left than he started with. Some broke when they were being washed. Some dropped to the floor and were cracked. And some just disappeared. But Menches never worried about that: His supplier always turned up with a new supply every day.

On one especially hot July day, Menches opened his stand prepared to face a very busy day. He needed lots of new dishes, but the supplier was late. Menches was down to a very low number of plates before noon. What, he wondered, would he do when the demand for ice cream increased with the arrival of the large noontime crowd?

His friend in the stand next to his, a man named Ernest Hamwi from Syria, was selling Zalabia, a sort of flat, crisp wafer that was popular in the Middle East. Menches thought he'd buy one of them for his lunch while he tried to think of a way to handle his disappearing dish problem. As he held the Zalabia, he noticed how easily it folded. It reminded him of how colored sheets of paper were rolled into cones to hold candies as birthday party favors when he was a little boy.

He thought, "*What if* I rolled the Zalabia into cones and put the ice cream into them?"

The idea was a fabulous success. People not only could eat the "dish" in which the ice cream was served, they could also walk around and enjoy the fair while enjoying their ice cream treat.

BIRTH OF A BABY FOOD

from THE PROBLEM SOLVERS
by Nathan Aaseng

One Sunday evening in the summer of 1927, Dan and Dorothy Gerber were getting ready to go out for the evening. They found it was taking them longer than they had hoped. Dorothy had to feed their seven-month-old daughter, Sally, before they left. Dan impatiently eyed the clock as Dorothy began to strain the peas.

Dorothy was tired of mashing vegetables through a strainer three times a day, seven days a week. She suggested that Dan try hand-straining the baby food himself. The container of peas, the strainer, and the bowl ended up in Dan's lap, and he discovered for himself what a slow, messy, frustrating process straining vegetables was. Within 24 hours, Dan was looking for a better way to make baby food.

Fortunately, the materials for a solution were near at hand. Dan and his father, Frank Gerber, owned a vegetable canning factory in their small town of Fremont, Michigan. Dorothy knew that the plant already had a machine that could puree tomatoes. She wondered if any of the equipment there could also strain baby food.

Before the advent of precooked baby food, parents had to
strain vegetables by hand, a lengthy and often frustrating process.
Gerber Products Company

When Dan went to work the next morning, he spent
much of the day adapting some of the plant machinery to
the task of straining peas. The more the Gerbers thought
about it, the more certain they were that other parents
hated the tedious straining process as much as they did.
Why not design machinery to do the job in the factory and
eliminate the task from the family kitchen?

The plan, however, had to be approved by the majority
owner of the factory, Dan's father. Frank Gerber knew the

Tired of making baby food at home, Dorothy Gerber urged her husband Dan to try to find a better way to make it.

Dan Gerber

risks involved in making products for babies. If the company ever made a mistake that caused trouble for a baby's delicate digestive system, the Fremont Canning Company could be ruined. Since the plant was doing well, it would have been easy for Frank to stick with what he was doing.

But the elder Gerber had never been one to stand still. He had risked using new processes before. With both his son and daughter-in-law arguing in favor of making strained foods, Frank Gerber gave Dan his approval.

Cautious with the family money, Dan took his time in laying the groundwork for his project. First he researched the market. Strained baby food was not a novel idea. Some brands were already on the market, but they were not selling well. These specialty products sold only in drugstores, and they cost so much that few people could afford them. National surveys showed that many people across the country were exasperated with straining baby food. If the Gerbers could maintain a high-quality product and keep it reasonably priced by selling large quantities in grocery stores, they were certain to be successful.

The next step was coming up with a good product. Frank and Dan spent nearly a year trying out various recipes and straining techniques. Babies of Fremont Canning Company employees, including Sally Gerber, sampled the concoctions and their responses were recorded.

In the fall of 1928, the Gerbers introduced their first five baby foods: peas, spinach, prunes, carrots, and vegetable soup. Dan then devised a clever plan to get the product into grocery stores. He placed an advertisement in *Good Housekeeping* magazine, offering to sell six cans of baby food for $1.00 to people who would send him the name of their local grocer. Armed with the directory of names this gave him, Dan approached the grocers and asked them to stock his products based on his evidence of the demand for baby food.

Recognizing the importance of a strong visual identity for their product, the Gerbers set up a contest for artists to submit pictures of a healthy, happy baby. One of the contestants, Dorothy Hope Smith, sent in a charcoal sketch with an attached note saying she would be happy to finish the picture if it was what the Gerbers wanted. Dan and

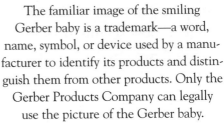

The familiar image of the smiling Gerber baby is a trademark—a word, name, symbol, or device used by a manufacturer to identify its products and distinguish them from other products. Only the Gerber Products Company can legally use the picture of the Gerber baby.

Gerber Products Company

Frank liked the sketch just as it was, and Smith's rough drawing became the famous Gerber baby.

Gerber baby food set off a storm of demand far greater than Dan had ever imagined possible. Within six months of beginning production, Gerber strained products could be found on grocery shelves across the country. The baby food did not stay long on the shelves, either. The Fremont Canning Company sold more than a half million cans of baby food during the first year of business.

Success breeds imitators, and the baby food market was no exception. Just four years after Dan Gerber broke new ground in this market, he faced more than 60 competitors. The company kept ahead of the competition by establishing a reputation as baby experts. Dorothy Gerber answered letters from consumers who wrote in with a variety of child-rearing concerns. Before long the company hired a nationally known dietician and other experts who wrote pamphlets and booklets on the care and feeding of babies.

In 1941 the name of the company was changed from the Fremont Canning Company to the Gerber Products

In 1938, Gerber hired dietician Dr. Lillian Storms to develop and test recipes for the company.

Company. Since that time, most United States parents have been happy to let food companies handle the inconvenience of mashing food for babies. Many families have given the task to Gerber, which now makes more than 187 varieties of baby foods.

Few people have been as successful as the Gerbers in "killing two birds with one stone." Not only did they get rid of one of their most dreaded chores, but they were able to make a fortune in the process.

TIN-PEDDLER

from FARMER BOY by Laura Ingalls Wilder

illustrated by Garth Williams

One evening after sunset Almanzo saw a white horse pulling a large, bright-red cart up the road, and he yelled,
"The tin-peddler's coming! The tin-peddler's coming!"

Alice ran out of the henhouse with her apron full of eggs. Mother and Eliza Jane came to the kitchen door. Royal popped out of the pump-house. And the young horses put their heads through the windows of their stalls and whinnied to the big white horse.

Nick Brown, the tin-peddler, was a jolly, fat man, who told stories and sang songs. In the springtime he went driving along all the country roads, bringing news from far and near.

His cart was like a little house, swinging on stout leather straps between four high wheels. It had a door on either side, and from its rear a platform slanted upward like a bird's tail, held in place by straps that went to the cart's top. There was a fancy railing all around the top of the cart, and the cart and the platform and the wheels were all painted bright red, with beautiful scrolls painted bright yellow. High in front rode Nick Brown, on a red seat above the rump of the sturdy white horse.

Almanzo and Alice and Royal and even Eliza Jane were waiting when the cart stopped by the kitchen porch, and Mother was smiling in the doorway.

"How do you do, Mr. Brown!" she called. "Put up your horse and come right in, supper's almost ready!" And Father called from the barn, "Drive into the Buggy-house, Nick, there's plenty of room!"

Almanzo unhitched the sleek, big horse and led him to water, then put him in a stall and gave him a double feed of oats and plenty of hay. Mr. Brown carefully currycombed and brushed him, and rubbed him down with clean cloths. He was a good horseman. After that he looked at all the stock and gave his opinion of it. He admired Star and Bright and praised Father's colts.

"You ought to get a good price for those coming four-year-olds," he said to Father. "Over by Saranac, the New York buyers are looking for driving-horses. One of them paid two hundred dollars apiece last week for a team not a mite better than these."

Almanzo could not speak while grown-ups were talking, of course. But he could listen. He didn't miss anything that Mr. Brown said. And he knew that the best time of all was coming after supper.

Nick Brown could tell more funny stories and sing more songs than any other man. He said so himself, and it was true.

"Yes, sir," he said, "I'll back myself, not alone against any man, but against any crowd of men. I'll tell story for story and sing song for song, as long as you'll bring men up against me, and when they're all done, I'll tell the last story and sing the last song."

Father knew this was true. He had heard Nick Brown do it, in Mr. Case's store in Malone.

So after supper they all settled down by the heater, and Mr. Brown began. It was after nine o'clock before anyone went to bed, and Almanzo's sides ached with laughing.

Next morning after breakfast Mr. Brown hitched the white horse to the cart and drove it up to the kitchen porch, and he opened the red doors.

Inside that cart was everything ever made of tin. On shelves along the walls were nests of bright tin pails, and pans, and basins, cake-pans, pie-pans, bread-pans, and dish-pans. Overhead dangled cups and dippers, skimmers and strainers, steamers, colanders, and graters. There were tin horns, tin whistles, toy tin dishes and patty-pans, there were all kinds of little animals made of tin and brightly painted.

Mr. Brown had made all these himself, in the winter-
time, and every piece was made of good thick tin, well
made and solidly soldered.

Mother brought the big rag-bags from the attic, and
emptied on the porch floor all the rags she had saved during the last year. Mr. Brown examined the good, clean rags
of wool and linen, while Mother looked at the shining tinware, and they began to trade.

For a long time they talked and argued. Shining tinware
and piles of rags were all over the porch. For every pile of

rags that Nick Brown added to the big pile, Mother asked more tinware than he wanted to trade her. They were both having a good time, joking and laughing and trading. At last Mr. Brown said,

"Well, ma'am, I'll trade you the milk-pans and pails, the colander and skimmer, and the three baking-pans, but not the dishpan, and that's my last offer."

"Very well, Mr. Brown," Mother said, unexpectedly. She had got exactly what she wanted. Almanzo knew she did not need the dishpan; she had set it out only to bargain with. Mr. Brown knew that, too, now. He looked surprised, and he looked respectfully at Mother. Mother was a good, shrewd trader. She had bested Mr. Brown. But he was satisfied, too, because he had got plenty of good rags for his tinware.

He gathered up the rags and tied them into a bale, and heaved the bale onto the slanting platform behind his cart. The platform and the railing around the top of the cart were made to hold the rags he took in trade.

Then Mr. Brown rubbed his hands together and looked around, smiling.

"Well now," he said, "I wonder what these young folks would like!"

He gave Eliza Jane six little diamond-shaped patty-pans to bake little cakes in, and he gave Alice six heart-shaped ones, and he gave Almanzo a tin horn painted red. They all said:

"Thank you, Mr. Brown!"

Then Mr. Brown climbed to his high seat and took up the reins. The big white horse stepped out eagerly, well fed and brushed and rested. The red cart went past the house and lurched into the road, and Mr. Brown began to whistle.

Mother had her tinware for the year, and Almanzo had his loud-squawking horn, and Nick Brown rode whistling away between the green trees and the fields. Until he came again next spring they would remember his news and laugh at his jokes, and behind the horses in the fields Almanzo would whistle the songs he had sung.

MEET LAURA INGALLS WILDER,
AUTHOR
Laura Ingalls Wilder first published her books when she was sixty-five years old. The story of the tin-peddler is from her book Farmer Boy, *which tells about the childhood of Wilder's husband, Almanzo. "These were family stories and I believed they should be preserved . . . I wanted children now to understand more about the beginning of things, to know what is behind the things they see—what it is that made America as they know it."*

Felés for Sale. 1972. Charles Searles.

Acrylic on canvas. Museum of the National Center of Afro-American Artists, Boston

Tinsmith's trade sign. c. 1825. Artist unknown.

Private collection. Photo: © America Hurrah, New York

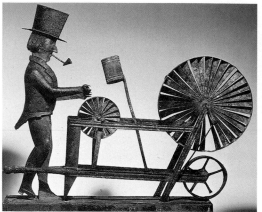

Poultry shop trade sign.
Date unknown.

Marble relief. Ostia Museum, Italy.
Photo: SCALA/Art Resource

Market Scene. Mid-20th century.
Rodrigue Mervilus.

Oil on canvas. Private collection.
Photo: © SuperStock

Buffalo Newsboy. 1853.
Thomas LeClear.

Oil on canvas, 24" x 20".
Charlotte A. Watson Fund, 1942, Albright-Knox
Art Gallery, Buffalo, New York

ANDREW CARNEGIE:
GIANT OF INDUSTRY
Mary Malone

*One of the most famous business leaders
of the late 1800s was Andrew Carnegie, owner of the United
States Steel Corporation. Andrew came to the United States
in 1848 from Scotland. His family was poor and he was
forced to work as a bobbin boy in a cotton mill. He earned
$1.20 a week, working twelve hours a day. At the
age of sixteen, Andrew became a telegraph operator. This led
to a job as a clerk for the Pennsylvania Railroad. Andrew
was intelligent and hard-working and was soon promoted to
manager. While working at the railroad, Andrew invested his
money and began buying stocks in various businesses.
Following the Civil War, Andrew used his money to help
rebuild the nation's railroads. To do this, he had to think of a
way to replace the wooden rails with something more sturdy
and longer-lasting. With the help of his brother and business
partner, Tom, Andrew eventually became one of
the richest men in the world.*

ndrew and Tom began to look for ways to improve the railroad.

One day they stood at the window of their office watching a work gang repairing the tracks.

"We lose too much time in repairing wooden rails," Andrew said.

Tom nodded. "Bridges, too."

Suddenly Andrew snapped his fingers. "I remember seeing a little iron bridge near Altoona! Why can't *we* build iron bridges instead of wooden ones? Iron bridges won't burn down or be washed away so easily in a flood."

"Let's try," Tom suggested. "First we'll find the man in Altoona who built the iron bridge."

When people heard of the Carnegies' plan, some said that iron couldn't support wide spans across a river or hold up heavy trains.

Andrew told them, "If we can't build a safe bridge, we won't build any."

This became his policy in all his work. Only the best quality was good enough for a Carnegie product.

The Bettmann Archive

An example of an iron bridge built by Carnegie in St. Louis, Missouri.
Brown Brothers

The iron bridges were successful. Then Andrew tried iron rails instead of the wooden ones that the railroads had been using for years. These, too, were a big improvement. Next, with his partners, Andrew built iron mills to produce the materials for rails and bridges. His business was booming. He began to invest some of his money in oil fields, and in insurance companies. Soon he was making so much money from his own companies that he decided to leave the Pennsylvania Railroad. He was only thirty years old, but from that time on he never worked for a salary from others. Young as he was, he could afford to be his own boss.

The railroads became Carnegie's best customers. They were growing bigger and bigger, crisscrossing the country from east to west and from west to east. More and more rails and bridges were needed. More iron was needed for the bridges and rails. More sleeping cars were being used—and more locomotives. Soon Andrew started another company to make locomotives. In all of the Carnegie companies, he was the chief partner.

It was time now, he decided, to move to New York City, the business capital of the country. He would be close to other business concerns and better able to sell the Carnegie products. His mother moved with him, and they lived in a large apartment in one of New York's best hotels. Tom remained in Pittsburgh as business manager of the Carnegie companies and moved into the house at Homewood with his new wife.

Andrew's business methods seemed daring to Tom and to some of the other partners. Andrew was always shrewd and practical, however. If he learned about another company that made a product similar to his, he did not waste time fighting but got the company to join him.

By this time he owned the original sleeping car business. But a man named George Pullman was making sleeping cars, too, and selling them to railroads in the West. He and Andrew both wanted to sell their cars to the big Union Pacific Railroad. Andrew went directly to Mr. Pullman and said, "Let's stop making fools of ourselves."

Surprised, Mr. Pullman asked Andrew, "What do you mean?"

Andrew smiled. "We are now working against each other. The railroads will beat us down. If we unite and become one company, we'll both move ahead."

Pullman railroad car compartment.

Mr. Pullman frowned. "What would you call the company?"

"Why, the Pullman Palace Car Company," Andrew replied promptly.

Mr. Pullman relaxed. The name pleased him. Besides, he knew that Carnegie was right. "I'll join you," he said. Together, they won a big contract from the Union Pacific.

Always, Carnegie searched restlessly for new ways to do things. He heard about a process used in England that made iron into steel. He went over to see how it was done and to meet the man who had invented it, Henry Bessemer. He saw a furnace where air was forced through crude iron, burning out carbon and other impurities in the iron. What was left was steel—a stronger, tougher metal.

Andrew returned home, excited by what he had seen. "We should start making steel at once," he told Tom and the other partners. "Just think what this means! Steel will replace iron just as iron replaced wood. We have no time to lose!"

The others were not interested. One of the partners said, "A few companies tried to use this Bessemer process and failed."

Tom nodded. "We've been successful because we worked hard and used sensible methods," he said. "Why risk what we've built up for this new method we're not sure of?"

Andrew laughed. "All right. I'll start a new company, with new partners!"

"This is no time to build, Andy," one of the partners warned. "We're going through a depression."

Andrew turned to him quickly. "It's the best time to build," he said. "I can do it more cheaply now. Then I'll be ready to take orders when prosperity returns."

While the others shook their heads and called him reckless, he continued, "I have the cash to construct the first steel works in America. And I'm going to do it!"

Carnegie had an unshakable faith in the future growth of America. He sold most of his stock in his other companies and put the money into a new steel plant. Then he went out and persuaded railroads to give him orders. He knew his customers and he gave them a fair price. With the new Bessemer process, Carnegie made steel the outstanding industry of Pittsburgh. His steel mills worked day and night, their great blast furnaces shooting flames high into the sky.

One of the reasons for Carnegie's success was his judgment of men. He picked good men to work for him. One of these was Captain Bill Jones. Andrew chose Bill Jones to manage the Edgar Thomson Steel Company. Then Carnegie bought the Homestead Mills. He now owned the largest steel complex in the world, with 30,000 workers. Big, brawny Bill Jones was a fighter as well as a worker. He knew the steel business and he was enthusiastic about the new Bessemer process. Under his leadership the men in the Edgar Thomson Steel Company became experts at making steel.

"I worked with Bill Jones!" was the proud boast of many Pittsburgh steel workers.

Carnegie thought so highly of Bill that he offered him a partnership in the company.

Bill looked down at the short, stocky little Scotsman. Then he shook his head. "No, thanks, Boss. I have enough to do looking after the mill."

Carnegie knew Bill would miss the men if he had to work in an office. "What would you like, then?" he asked, smiling.

Bill laughed. "Just pay me a whopping big salary if you think I'm worth it."

Without any hesitation, Carnegie agreed. "It's yours. From now on, Bill, you'll get the same salary as the President of the United States."

When his partners complained, Carnegie only said, "Where would you find another Bill Jones?"

One day in 1889 Bill himself shut down the steel mills. "Johnstown is flooded!" Bill shouted to his workers. "They need our help!"

After many days of heavy rain, Lake Conemaugh, in the Allegheny Mountains above the town of Johnstown, had overflowed. The old earthwork dam, which was supposed to hold back the lake waters from the valley below, gave way. The water roared down on Johnstown, smashing everything in its path. Thousands of people were drowned in one of the worst disasters in American history.

Bill Jones and his men piled into freight cars and rode the 70 miles from Pittsburgh to Johnstown. They all worked for days helping the homeless and bewildered people there.

Later that year the Edgar Thomson Works was the scene of a terrible accident. One of the furnaces exploded, killing six men who were near it. Bill Jones was one of them.

Some time later when Andrew Carnegie built his home in New York, he placed a big picture of Bill Jones on the wall. To everyone who saw it hanging there, he said, "*He* was the greatest steel maker of them all."

DOROTHY BRUNSON:
THE MAKING OF AN ENTREPRENEUR
from WOMEN MAKING HISTORY
by Jacqueline Paris-Chitanvis
illustrated by Bill Fricke

When Dorothy Brunson was growing up in Harlem during the 1940s, she appeared to be like most of the other children in her neighborhood. She played, fought with her friends, got into mischief and generally enjoyed growing up. But in one respect she was different. She had a secret passion—reading. She would read anything from *Peter Pan* to the Hardy Boys, to Shakespeare. And it was through reading that she came to believe that she—a poor, black child of the ghetto—could be anything she wanted to be, do anything she wanted to do.

"I read a lot of black history and there was something so unique about the black experience that it inspired me," she explains. "My heroine was Mary McLeod Bethune. Just to read her life story was so fascinating. And the more I read it, the more I thought, 'If that can happen [to her], why not to me?' "

WGTW-TV 48

And happen it did. Today Dorothy Brunson is worth millions. She has owned several enterprises, including Brunson Communications, a television station, and three radio stations—in Atlanta, Baltimore and Wilmington, North Carolina—and Citimedia, a company in New York that secures national advertisers for radio. "I never thought about not accomplishing things," she says, "because all my heroes [in books] succeeded."

179

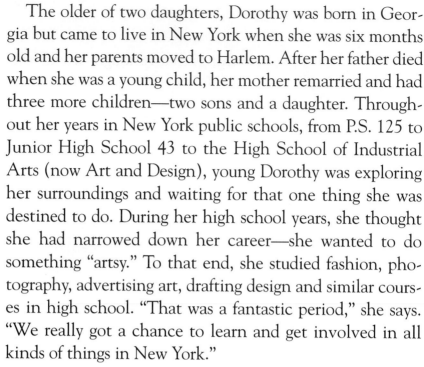

The older of two daughters, Dorothy was born in Georgia but came to live in New York when she was six months old and her parents moved to Harlem. After her father died when she was a young child, her mother remarried and had three more children—two sons and a daughter. Throughout her years in New York public schools, from P.S. 125 to Junior High School 43 to the High School of Industrial Arts (now Art and Design), young Dorothy was exploring her surroundings and waiting for that one thing she was destined to do. During her high school years, she thought she had narrowed down her career—she wanted to do something "artsy." To that end, she studied fashion, photography, advertising art, drafting design and similar courses in high school. "That was a fantastic period," she says. "We really got a chance to learn and get involved in all kinds of things in New York."

After high school, Brunson attended Tennessee State University in Nashville for about a year and a half. Her first college experience wasn't very noteworthy, she says, because she spent most of her time "playing tennis, swimming and playing bridge." Deciding that she "really didn't want to do all those things," Brunson returned to New York. "By that time I realized that I had not really focused," she says. "I wanted to do something that was going to make money."

Although she had enjoyed the creative classes she took in high school, there was another side of her that she had been fighting. "A very structured, very disciplined, very exacting kind of a person," she says. "It was that side that I kept running into problems with. I took dance lessons, I took music, I took all the things that I thought would help me pursue an arts career. But I didn't like the unsureness of it. Where would I be next week? Next year? I didn't like the vagabond feeling. So I decided to study something that would be more practical."

She went back to school and studied accounting and finance, taking courses at Pace College and Empire State College in New York. She eventually received a bachelor's degree from Empire State in the late 1960s. Throughout her college years, Brunson worked at a variety of jobs. "One of my jobs was dealing with layouts for newspaper ads," she says. "I was supposed to get the ads, look at them, make sure they were placed properly and make sure we billed properly. That was really nice, because it was the first time that I was doing something that was a combination of both my high school experience and my college training. It was through that job that I first began to learn a little bit about the media. I began to see that a newspaper was not only about journalism, that there was an advertising side.

"It was from that job in 1962 that I went to radio. At that time Sonderling Broadcasting, which owned several radio stations, was looking for someone to be an assistant comptroller [at WWRL]. They wanted someone black and they wanted someone whom they could give a title to because they were changing over from a foreign language station to a black-program format. They wanted someone in management that they could show to the community [to demonstrate] that they were responsive. They had to find someone who knew about accounting and advertising and who at least had some understanding of radio.

"During that time, I was doing a lot of volunteer work in the community—NAACP, Urban League—and someone suggested that I go over for an interview. At first I said 'No, I love my job because I'm involved in advertising, promotions and layouts, and I'm planning budgets. I've found a little niche.' But I went anyway and they offered me the job."

After only three months as the assistant, Brunson was asked to take over as comptroller. She says the promotion came so quickly because she was willing to work harder than anyone else in the department and to tackle any job— whether she knew how to do it or not. As comptroller, she would work even harder.

"I took on project after project after project," she says. "They would say, 'Do you know how to do this?' and I'd say, 'Sure,' and then I'd run out and get a book. I went back to school and took courses—communications, management, everything. I never told anyone that I couldn't do something. I worked weekends, I worked nights. I would go home, and when I knew everyone had left, I'd go back and work until 3 or 4 in the morning because I had to get a project done. I didn't want anyone to know that I didn't know how to do it. After I took over the department, we grew from a station that was doing about $700,000 worth of

[advertising] billing to one that was doing close to $5 million. My department originally had five or six people; I took it down to three. I put in a computer system and went to computer school."

During the seven years she was with Sonderling Broadcasting, Brunson continued her career climb. After a year as comptroller, she moved to assistant general manager and then to corporate liaison. In 1971, she left Sonderling to become a partner in a new Madison Avenue advertising agency. The partnership, however, was short-lived and Brunson sold her share of the business. "We couldn't get along," she says with a laugh, "but we're still friends."

For about a year and a half Brunson worked as a consultant in radio and advertising. It was during this time that she also decided to start a family. "By that time I was thirty plus and everyone was saying, 'If you don't have children. . . .' Well, I didn't even get married until I was 26," she says. But by the end of 1972, Brunson had given birth to two sons.

One day that year, she got a call from a friend who asked her if she would be willing to invest in a radio station (WLIB-AM in New York) owned by Inner City Broadcasting. She also was asked if she would pull together a group of investors. "I said fine, I'll do that," she recalls, "but nobody told me that they were on their way to bankruptcy. I got some investors, about eight or nine friends, and we invested about $5,000 or $10,000 each."

But getting the investors didn't help Inner City's finances. Six months after they were in business, the bank holding the

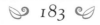

start-up loan gave Inner City an ultimatum: pay up the loan or hire a qualified general manager for the radio station. They turned to Brunson, and after much arm-twisting she reluctantly agreed to accept the position. When she took over as general manager, the station was $1 million in debt.

Brunson immediately cut the staff of around 35—she considered it much too inflated—down to eight people. She then gave the remaining employees raises and redesigned their jobs. She also restructured the station, made it more community oriented and set about repaying the bank loan a little at a time. A year later, she approached the bank about another $1 million loan to buy an FM station, WBLS, that she hoped would bring in more money. And even though the initial loan was outstanding, the bank, which liked what she had done so far, approved the additional loan. By the time Brunson left Inner City in 1979, it owned seven radio stations and was valued at close to $50 million.

Despite earning a six-figure salary, Brunson left Inner City because she felt it was time she started using her talents to build her own business. With $3 million in loans, she purchased WEBB, a struggling radio station in Baltimore and poured $250,000 into revitalizing it. Two years later, she purchased WIGO in Atlanta, and was on her way.

Today, Brunson also owns a television station.
WGTW-TV 48

Brunson attributes much of her success to being goal-oriented and hard-working—traits, she says, passed on to her by her mother. "My mother is a great believer in the idea that if you trust in the Lord, work hard and do things right, you're going to win," says Brunson. "All of us believed that, and we were always hard-working children. We worked during school and we worked to put ourselves through college. There was never any thought of doing otherwise. You worked at it, you did it long enough and you'd get it. And that's what we did. On that point my mother was steadfast, very steadfast. She always found a way. If we wanted to go to the prom and she didn't have money, she found a way. She would say, 'Don't worry about it.' And that was like saying go. That's the thing that gave us children strength."

BUSINESS IS
LOOKING UP

Barbara Aiello and Jeffrey Shulman
illustrated by Marcy Ramsey

*Renaldo Rodriguez, a visually impaired eleven-year-old,
needs money to buy a special type of calculator for the blind.
He decides he can earn the money by starting a business and
shares his idea with his best friend, Jinx.*

"Jinx!" I shouted when she answered the phone. I sure
was excited about my business idea. "It's me! Renaldo.
Renaldo Rodriguez!"

"Renaldo, you're the only Renaldo I know," Jinx said.
"And you don't have to holler! I can hear you."

I explained the whole idea to her—"R.R. Stepcards" I
called it. That was a pretty clever name, even I have to
admit. I told her how I would make and sell cards for people who had step-families: birthday cards, get well cards,
Valentine cards—the list was endless!

"What do you think, Jinx? Am I going to be Woodburn's
first millionaire?"

There was silence on the other end. I could tell Jinx was
thinking about it. She always thinks about things before

she gives her opinion. And she always thinks about what other people might think. "Opposing viewpoints," she calls them. Jinx does a lot of thinking.

"Well," she finally asked, "have you done any marketing research?"

"Marketing research?"

"Have you thought about your investment?"

"Investment?"

Jinx was on a roll. I felt doomed.

"Oh, how will you advertise?"

I felt it coming, but I couldn't stop it. "Advertise?" I said. "Just listen to me," I thought to myself, "Renaldo Rodriguez, the human echo!"

Research? Investment? Advertising? "Jinx," I said, "this is starting to sound like work! Explain this stuff to me."

I knew Jinx was excited. I could hear the excitement in her voice. "Look," she began, "marketing research is the first thing you do. You find out if someone else has already thought of your idea. You find out if there's such a thing as a stepcard. If there's not, then you can figure out your investment. That's how much money you want to spend to get the business started."

"Spend?" I said. "But I want to *make* money, Jinx."

"I know," Jinx said in her most patient voice. "But you can't get something for nothing. We will have to buy markers and paper, maybe even paints and stencils, too. That's our investment."

"*Our* investment? When did it become *our* investment?"

"Renaldo, this is an excellent idea," Jinx continued. "But there's a lot to do. You're going to need a partner." And I didn't even have the time to say "A partner?" before Jinx jumped in again. "Hmmmm . . . I do like the sound of it," she said. "Yes, 'R.R. and J.B. Stepcards.' I like the sound of it very much."

And you know what? So did I. With J.B. as my partner, I was more excited than ever—so excited that I couldn't get to sleep that night. I turned my pillow to the cold side a hundred times until I gave up trying to sleep. I got out my stylus and slate and started to write: "R.R. and J.B. Stepcards. For Your Favorite Stepfriend." There were stepfathers, stepmothers, stepbrothers, stepsisters, stepgrandmothers— the list went on and on. "For All Occasions." There were birthdays, anniversaries, graduations, holidays—and so many more. I started counting our profits. I couldn't help it.

"Excuse me, Mr. Businessman," Josue said, hiding a big yawn. "Mom already came in here. She made me stop reading. We're supposed to be asleep, you know."

Josue was right. Mom doesn't let us read or write after lights out. But, you see, I don't have to sneak under the covers with a flashlight the way Josue does.

"I'm not reading," I told Josue. "This, my little brother, is marketing research—I think."

"It looks like reading to me. It's not fair. I ought to tell on you!" Josue climbed out of bed to get a better look. "Just what kind of business is this anyway?"

"None of *your* business," I said firmly. And I closed my slate. I wasn't taking any chances on someone stealing the

business idea of the century, certainly not a nosy little brother. I turned my pillow over for the last time.

"Let's go to sleep."

The next day was Saturday, and with lots of kids from Woodburn, Jinx and I headed for the mall. We take turns delivering the "Woodburn Flyer" to the stores at the Woodburn Shopping Center. The "Flyer" is the free newspaper that tells about all the things happening at Woodburn. Then it's time for fun.

But this Saturday was different. Today, there were no video games, no french fries, no window-shopping. Today, we were all business.

I knew we were near Calloway's Cards and Gifts when I smelled the tempting aroma of cheese, tomato sauce, and special toppings. Polotti's Pizza Palace was just next door to the card store.

"I don't think I can do the marketing research on an empty stomach. How about a business lunch?" I was tapping my cane toward the sweet smell of Polotti's.

"Renaldo," Jinx said sternly, "we don't have much time."

"Okay. Okay," I said. "Give me your arm." Jinx was right. We really didn't have much time. "It will be faster for me to walk alongside you—and less temptation, too."

There must have been a thousand different kinds of cards in Calloway's, and each one was cornier or mushier than the last. One thing about those cards, though—they really cracked us up!

"Look at this one, Renaldo," Jinx said.

"*To My Daughter and Her Husband on This Special Day,*" Jinx read. She described the card to me. "It's big," she said, passing it to me.

"It's almost the size of our spelling notebook," I said, feeling around the edges of the card.

"It has two pink hearts with bows on them. Two white doves are holding the ends of the ribbons in their mouths. It looks like the words *Happy Anniversary* are coming right out of their beaks," Jinx giggled.

I could feel the raised lines of the hearts, the bows, and the birds. "Yuk," I said, "it sounds pretty corny to me."

"Listen to this, Renaldo."

To My Daughter and Her Husband on This Special Day:
'Like two white doves are lovers true,
Like two pink hearts forever new.
I hope this day will always view
A ribbon of happiness just for you.'

"Double yuk," I said. "Who buys this mush?"

"Here's another one, Renaldo," Jinx said. "*Congratulations on Your New Baby!* It has a picture of a stork with a baby in a diaper hanging in its mouth."

"It must look so silly," I said, trying hard not to giggle too loudly.

"It gets worse." Jinx was cracking up. "When you open up the card, the stork drops the baby—plop!—right on somebody's doorstep!"

"It sounds like a wet diaper to me!" I squealed. Jinx was laughing, too. But then she suddenly stopped. I could tell she was really thinking.

"But, Renaldo," she said in a serious voice, "somebody buys these cards, and"—she was getting very excited—"there are no stepcards!"

Now I was getting excited, too. We did a high-five right there in Calloway's. "We're going to be rich!" we both shouted.

"C'mon, Renaldo," Jinx urged, "let's go home and get to work."

"Be sure to save an extra large pepperoni and sausage for Woodburn's youngest millionaires!" I shouted when we passed Polotti's.

Getting to work was not as easy as it sounded.

Jinx and I had to buy the paper for the cards. We put our money together for an investment of twelve dollars and thirty-two cents. ("That's a lot of french fries," I thought.) We had to decide what kind of cards to make. We had to think of designs for the front of the cards and messages to go inside. We had to find a way to let people know about "R.R. and J.B. Stepcards."

Let's face it: We had a lot to learn about starting a business.

When I have more questions than answers, I always turn to the expert—my Mom. "Mom," I said when she got home from work, "Jinx and I need to speak to an old hand in the business world."

"Good luck finding one," she replied as she started to take off the running shoes she wears to work.

"No, Mom," I explained, "I meant you."

"Oh," she said, looking up. "What can this 'old hand' do for you?"

My Mom knows about business, especially bad businesses. She works in an office helping people who bought things that don't work or aren't safe. I figured if she knew all about bad businesses, she could tell us how to start a good one.

Jinx and I explained our business idea. "How do we get started?" Jinx asked.

"How do we make lots of money?" (I guess you can figure out who asked that one!)

Mom thought for a while. Then she spoke slowly. "Jinx, Renaldo, starting and running a business is not so easy. It's more than just making money. A successful business needs a good product to sell or a useful service to offer. And a successful businessman—or businesswoman—thinks about the customer all the time. Ask yourself: 'What do they want?' 'How can my product or my service help them?'"

Jinx and I were trying to listen to all of this, but it wasn't easy. We *did* have a lot to learn.

"Now, you two have a good product," Mom continued. "I'm proud of you for coming up with this idea. But a good idea is not enough. You need to plan carefully."

"What do we do, Mrs. Rodriguez?" Jinx asked.

"Well," Mom said, "you need to figure out how much money you'll need to get started and where the money will come from. You need to decide who will do the work and, believe me, a business *is* work. Now, if you're still interested in 'R.R. and J.B. Stepcards,' let's make a plan!"

"Always ask the expert," I shouted. I could hear the rubber soles of Mom's shoes make that familiar squeegy sound. Mom wears business suits and running shoes every day to work. Dad says she's dressed for success from her head to her knees—but her feet are dressed for failure! That always makes me laugh.

With Mom's help we really got started. Jinx and I used our "investment" to buy paper, paints, markers, and stencils. We worked every day after school. We took turns with the stencils to make the designs. We'd take a small roller and dip it into a bright color of paint. When we'd smooth the roller over the stencil, there was a butterfly or flower or other designs. Jinx said they looked great!

I liked making up the words for our stepcards. I thought of some pretty good ones, if I must say so myself.

To My Stepfather:
'Getting to know you hasn't been half bad.
I'm glad Mom picked you to be my Stepdad!'

Well, I didn't say they were great cards.

To My Stepsister:
'You have two families, I know that's true.
But I want you to know that I love you, too!'

All right, so Renaldo Rodriguez has a mushy side. Don't rub it in!

At the end of just one week, Jinx and I had 34 cards ready to go.

"To go where?" I asked.

"Where else?" Jinx said. "Why, the Woodburn School and Community Center!" It was time to advertise, and Woodburn was the place to start.

The Woodburn School was the oldest school building in the city. It almost closed the year before. There just weren't enough kids to fill it up, I guess. That's why the school board decided to add a Community Center. Now there was a day-care room for little kids and an activity center for older people, too. Woodburn is like a little city all its own.

The first thing on Monday morning Jinx and I marched down to Woodburn and showed our cards to Mr. Mohammadi, the assistant principal. Boy, was he excited!

"A sound idea," he said. "A very sound business idea. And you'll get a real education in the bargain. A real education. How can I help?"

We explained that advertising "R.R. and J.B. Stepcards" was the next part of our business plan.

"Let's see now." Mr. Mohammadi was thinking out loud. "You can put advertisements in the school newspaper, posters in the Senior Center, flyers to go home. . . ." Mr. Mohammadi was pacing the floor and spouting new ideas faster than . . . faster than . . . well, faster than Jinx and I could write them down.

"This is going to be a snap," I predicted. "I should have started a business years ago. Think of all the time I've wasted in school!"

That stopped Mr. Mohammadi in his tracks. "Just a little business joke," I gulped.

If you want to start a business, take it from me: advertise! With Mr. Mohammadi's help, Jinx and I spread the word about "R.R. and J.B. Stepcards." Believe it or not, within one week, we sold 17 of our cards and had orders for 20 more. That's 37 cards! We'd make back all the money we spent on supplies. We'd even have some left over.

"Now that we'll have a little extra money, why not buy some stickers and glitter?" Jinx suggested. "Let's make the cards even prettier."

I was thinking about my calculator. I wanted to buy it as soon as I could. "But, Renaldo," Jinx said, "if we make our cards prettier, we'll sell more and make more money."

That made sense. Then I could buy the calculator and a new pair of soccer shoes.

"Don't forget," Jinx reminded me, "we have to pay to use the copying machine." We had to make copies of the advertisement Mr. Mohammadi was going to send home with the kids.

"And we need copies to take to the Senior Center, too," I told Jinx. I remember Mom saying, "You have to spend some money to make money." We thought that advertising was the best way to get more sales.

We thought right! Every day more orders came in the mail.

This was going to be a snap.

Jinx and I had to work every afternoon that week to fill the orders. And every day more orders came in.

Jeremy Kendall's stepsisters had their birthdays coming up, so he ordered two cards from "R.R. and J.B. Stepcards," along with a special card for his stepmother. Mrs. Rothman (from the Senior Center) told us her son had just married a woman with twin boys, and she needed birthday cards for her stepgrandchildren. Roger Neville's stepfather was in the hospital, so he wanted a special get well card. And Joanne Spinoza's mother, Lena, wanted a stepcousin Valentine.

Phew! Jinx and I could hardly believe how well our business was going. We just didn't expect how happy people would be with our cards.

"You know, Jinx," I said, as I lined up the paint jars, "it's nice to give people something special."

Jinx agreed. "Jeremy told me that our card really helped him tell his stepmother how much he liked her."

"No kidding?"

"You know what else? He said she cried a little when she read it, and then she said she really liked him, too."

"Hey," I said, "making people happy is a pretty good way to make a living."

SALT

Harve Zemach
illustrated by Margot Zemach

Long ago there lived a merchant who had three sons. The first was Fyodor, the second Vasily, and the third Ivan—Ivan the Fool.

This merchant was rich. He sent his ships over the ocean in all directions to trade goods in foreign lands. Once he loaded two ships with precious furs, wax, and honey, and sent them sailing with his two elder sons. But when Ivan asked for the same, the merchant refused, saying: "You would do nothing but sing songs to the moon, and try to make the fishes dance, and come home without your head."

However, when he saw how much his son wanted to go, he gave him a ship with the very cheapest cargo of beams and boards.

Ivan prepared for the journey, set sail, and soon caught up with his brothers. They sailed together for a day or two,

until a strong wind came up and blew Ivan's ship away into uncharted seas.

The wind blew Ivan and his crew to the north and to the south. At last they reached an island. Ivan stepped out upon the shore and found a path which led to the top of a mountain. There he discovered that this mountain was not made of rock, nor of sand, nor of stone, but of salt—pure Russian salt.

Without delay he ordered his sailors to throw away all the boards and beams, and to load the ship with salt. As soon as this was done, Ivan set forth once more.

After a long time or a short time, either nearby or far away, the ship arrived at a large city. Ivan went into the city to bow before the king and request permission to trade his merchandise. He took a bundle of the salt with him. The king greeted him in a friendly manner and heard his request.

"And what kind of goods do you sell?" asked the king.

"Russian salt, Your Majesty," said Ivan, showing him the contents of his bundle.

The king had never heard of salt. The people of his kingdom ate all their food without salt. When he saw what Ivan showed him, he thought it was only white sand.

"Well, little brother," he said to Ivan, "we have all we need of this. No one will pay you money for it."

Ivan turned away feeling very disappointed. Then he thought to himself: "Why don't I go to the king's kitchen and see how the cooks prepare the food and what kind of salt they use." He went and watched the cooks running back and forth, boiling and roasting and pouring and mixing. But no one put a single grain of salt in the food.

Ivan waited his chance and then secretly poured the right amount of salt into all the stews and sauces.

When the first dish was served to the king, he ate of it and found it more tasty then ever before. The second dish was served, and he liked it even better.

Then the king called for his cooks and said to them: "In all the years that I have been king, you have never cooked me such a delicious meal. How did you do it?"

The cooks answered: "Your Majesty, we cooked the same as ever. But the merchant who asked your permission to trade was watching us. Perhaps he added something to the food."

"Send for him!" commanded the king.

Then Ivan, the merchant's son, was brought before the king. He fell on his knees and confessed his guilt. "Forgive

me, Your Majesty," he begged. "I put Russian salt in all the stews and sauces. That's the way we do it in my country."

"And what is the price of this salt?" asked the king.

Ivan realized his advantage and said: "Not very much— for two measures of salt, give me one measure of silver and one of gold."

The king agreed to this price and bought the entire cargo. Ivan filled his ship with silver and gold and made ready to sail for home.

Now, the king had a daughter, a beautiful princess. Attended by her maid servants, she went down to the port to see the Russian ship. Ivan the Fool just then was strumming a tune. The melody reached the ears of the princess, and its sweetness entered her heart.

It was not long before Ivan and the beautiful princess stood

together before the king to receive his blessing. To the sound of trumpets and the cheers of the king's subjects, Ivan and the princess departed from the city and sailed forth on a favorable wind.

For a long time, for a short time, Ivan and the princess sailed the sea. Then his elder brothers appeared across his path. They learned of his good luck and were very jealous.

They boarded his ship, seized him, and threw him into the sea. Then they divided the booty; Fyodor, the eldest brother, took the princess, and Vasily, the second brother, took the ship full of silver and gold.

Now, it happened that when they flung Ivan from the ship, one of the boards that he himself had thrown into the sea was floating nearby. He grabbed hold of this board and

for a long time was tossed upon the waves. Finally he was carried to an unknown island. No sooner had he landed on the shore than along came a gloomy giant with an enormous mustache, from which hung a huge pair of mittens, drying after the rain.

"What do you want here?" asked the giant. Ivan told him everything that had happened.

The gloomy giant sighed and said: "Come along, I will carry you home. Tomorrow your eldest brother is to marry the princess. Sit on my back."

The giant lifted Ivan, set him on his back, and raced across the sea. Soon Ivan could see his native land ahead, and moments later they arrived. The giant put him down, saying: "Now promise not to boast to anyone about riding on my back. Don't try to make fun of me. If you do, I shall grab you up and toss you back into the sea."

Ivan, the merchant's son, promised not to boast, thanked the giant, and went home.

He arrived just as the wedding procession was about to enter the church. When the princess saw him, she cried aloud and tore herself away from Fyodor, the eldest brother.

"This is the one I must marry," she said, "and not the other."

"What's that?" asked the father.

Ivan told him everything—how he had traded the salt, how he had won the favor of the princess, and how his brothers had thrown him into the sea.

The father got very angry at his elder sons, called them scoundrels, and married Ivan to the princess.

There now began a joyful feast. The guests ate and drank and made merry. The men began to boast, some about their strength, some about their riches, some about their beautiful wives. And Ivan the Fool happily boasted too: "Listen to

this! I really have something to boast about! A giant carried me piggyback across the sea!"

As soon as he said these words, the giant appeared at the gate.

"Ah, Ivan!" said the gloomy giant. "You promised not to boast about me. Now what have you done?"

"Forgive me!" cried Ivan. "It was not really I that boasted, but my happiness."

"Come, show me what you mean," said the giant. "What do you mean by happiness?"

Then Ivan took up his mandolin, and played and danced the best he knew how. And his playing and dancing was so filled with happiness that all the guests danced and clapped their hands. And soon the gloomy giant let himself smile and kept time to the music with his feet.

"Well, Ivan," he said at last, "now I know what happiness is. You may boast about me all you like."

So the wedding feast continued, and the giant departed, and Ivan the Fool and the beautiful princess lived happily ever after.

MEET MARGOT ZEMACH, ILLUSTRATOR

When *illustrating her books, Margot Zemach commented:
"Humor is the most important thing to me—it's what I'm thinking about. If I can make it beautiful, too—so much the better!
I always think, when I'm drawing the view of a town or inside a
hut: 'Would I have liked to live there?' To a certain extent,
one can invent one's own styles of dress and house shapes. But
things have to be made real. The food has to be what you'd want
to eat, the bed has to be what you'd get into right away."*

BIBLIOGRAPHY

From Rags to Riches: People Who Started Businesses from Scratch by Nathan Aaseng. The founders of great companies have sometimes come from very humble beginnings. Learn about some of these famous entrepreneurs.

The Glorious Whitewasher (adapted from Mark Twain's *The Adventures of Tom Sawyer* in *Plays*) by Walter Hackett. Tom makes his job sound so appealing that his friends pay for the privilege to do his work for him!

Henry Reed's Baby-Sitting Service by Keith Robertson. Will their babysitting business be a success? Henry and Midge again team up to make money.

It's Not Fair! by Susie Hoch Morgensten. It's a long climb to the top of the business world for Stacey, a ten-year-old entrepreneur.

Kid Power by Susan Beth Pfeffer. Running a business isn't easy. Janie learns about profits, expenses, and advertising as she tries to make her business work.

Lyddie by Katherine Paterson. To gain her independence, Lyddie, a poor Vermont farm girl in the 1840s, goes to work in a textile mill. Can she survive the harsh working conditions?

Max Malone Makes a Million by Charlotte Herman. Max and his friend Gordy are frustrated by their attempts to get rich. Yet their neighbor Austin makes money with no effort. Can they do it, too?

The Toothpaste Millionaire by Jean Merrill. How can a person make a million dollars? Read and discover how one kid did it.

THE MAYOS

ELIZABETH BLACKWELL

FU HSI

MARIE CURIE

EDWARD JENNER

WALTER REED

DANIEL HALE WILLIAMS

JONAS SALK

GALEN

The bubonic plague swept through Milan, Italy, in the 1600s.

MEDICINE:
PAST AND PRESENT
A. W. Carus

EARLY MEDICINE

Imagine you are living in Italy a few hundred years ago. One day, your friend next door gets sick. His mother and brother become ill the following day, and that night all three of them die. Neighbors all around you are sick—and dying. You don't know who might be next. It could even be you or your parents.

In those days, this nightmare is what life was like. In the middle of the fourteenth century, an epidemic called the Black Plague swept across Europe, Asia, and Africa. It killed about 75 million people, wiping out more than a third of Europe's population. While the disease spared some towns and villages, it killed nearly everyone in others. There was little warning, and those who caught the disease were dead within a few days.

Getting sick was always scary, not just during epidemics like the Black Plague. Death was never far away. People could fall ill and die at any moment, and no one would know why. Most people did not live to be very old. The average life expectancy was only thirty or forty years, about half what it is now in the United States.

For most of human history, people did not know what caused diseases. They could not see germs, so they didn't realize germs existed. Even after germs were discovered, it took a long time to connect them up with various diseases. It took even longer for people to understand how to keep germs from making people sick.

Before people knew about germs, they had other ideas about what caused diseases. Mostly, these ideas involved some kind of magical powers. It is easy to understand why people would believe such ideas. Diseases were terrifying and mysterious. Often there seemed to be no pattern to them. Why did some people die young and others get old? Why did some wounds get infected and others heal? Why did epidemics kill some people and not others? Without knowing about germs, it was easy to believe anything that might make a difference and possibly save a life.

So, it was a new idea when a few people suggested, in Greece about 2,500 years ago, that the human body is predictable and that diseases have natural causes and reasonable explanations. Hippocrates is the best known of these

people. Because this basic idea is so important, he is called the Father of Medicine. Hippocrates was sure that he could find reasons for illness by closely studying the human body and observing diseases. He also thought that people could understand the way the body worked.

Hippocrates' teachings are still studied today.
The Bettmann Archive

We now know that Hippocrates was on the right track. But when he lived, and for a long time afterwards, his idea was no more than a guess. And often it didn't seem like a very good guess (Hippocrates had lived nearly 2,000 years before the Black Plague and his beliefs still had very little support). So most people went on believing their old ideas and attempting to use magic to cure diseases. Sometimes the things they did had good results, even though the ideas about why these things worked were wrong. For example, when the ancient Chinese used herbs and the ancient Egyptians used moldy bread on wounds, they found that infections healed. Some Native-American people knew that chewing willow tree bark would help reduce pain. And many people knew that a doctor could help just by soothing patients and taking good care of them.

But Hippocrates' basic idea went on being not much more than a guess for a long time. Around 1600, things began to change. An Englishman named William Harvey discovered that blood in human and animal bodies doesn't just sit there. It moves, or circulates, all through the body every few minutes. And the heart is the pump that makes it move. This was an important breakthrough because it made sense of many things that had long been known about the heart and blood, but had never been pulled together. So it was an important step toward making Hippocrates' guess look more reasonable. A lot of seemingly mysterious and unrelated facts turned out to have a simple and natural explanation.

The discovery of germs and how they cause diseases took much longer. The first step was to realize that there *were* animals so tiny that they couldn't be seen by the naked eye. This step was taken by a Dutchman named Anton van Leeuwenhoek in 1674. After he heard of microscopes that magnified small objects, he made himself a very powerful one. He used it to look at water from a nearby pond and was amazed to find tiny animals swimming around in it. No human being had ever seen them before! He found many different kinds of microbes, as these tiny animals are called today, and became famous for this discovery. Ever since 1300, people had sometimes thought that such tiny living things might cause diseases. But Leeuwenhoek did not know of this idea. He did not suspect that the microbes he saw could cause the diseases that kill people. But now people knew that microbes really existed.

One of Leeuwenhoek's microscopes.

© Copyright Museum Boerhaave, Leiden

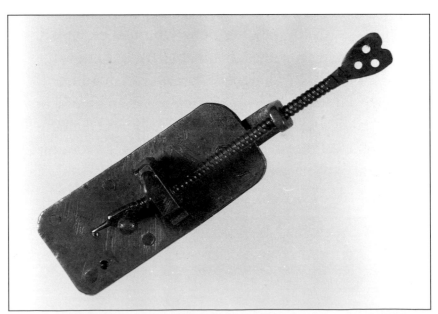

Another big step was taken around 1800 by an English doctor named Edward Jenner. He believed Hippocrates' guess; he was sure that diseases had natural causes. One particularly terrifying disease at that time was smallpox, which killed most people who got it. The few who recovered were left with scars on their faces and bodies but never got the disease again. Jenner guessed that the body developed some means to fight the disease, so that if it were invaded by smallpox again, the infection could not survive. He tried to think of a way of getting the body to develop these antibodies (as they are now called) to attack the disease without having to get smallpox first.

He knew that among cattle there was a disease called cowpox, which was similar to the human disease of smallpox. Humans could also get cowpox, but it rarely killed them and left no permanent scars. Jenner heard it said among country people in some parts of England that if you got cowpox, you would never get smallpox. Jenner decided to find out if this was true. He guessed that once the body developed antibodies to cowpox, the same antibodies would be able to fight off smallpox. He infected some people with cowpox, waited until they recovered, and then tried to infect them with smallpox. (This test was dangerous. Such experiments wouldn't be tried today!) The people didn't get ill. They had developed the antibodies, and they would not catch smallpox. They were immune to the disease.

So, Jenner had discovered a way of preventing small-pox. For the first time ever, doctors could do something to prevent a disease. And they had evidence that whatever caused smallpox could be defeated by something the body developed for itself. But they still didn't know what actually caused the disease. For centuries, people had been guessing that microbes, or germs, caused smallpox. No one made the actual connection between germs and disease until Louis Pasteur, a French chemist, conducted some experiments in the mid-1800s.

While Pasteur was doing his experiments, other scientists were discovering many different microbes. One kind of very small microbe, shaped like a rod or stick, was called bacterium, after the Greek word for stick. Pasteur carefully followed these discoveries and learned a lot about different types of bacteria. But before he could make the connection

Louis Pasteur in his lab.
© Erich Lessing/Art Resource

between these bacteria (or germs) and diseases, he had a more difficult job. Pasteur had to dispel, or prove wrong, an old belief that was standing in the way of his research.

Many people believed that living things could grow from nonliving things. They thought that rats grew from pieces of cheese, rotting meat turned into worms, and animals grew out of water. This idea, called spontaneous generation, seems silly to us now. But, it is easy to see why people believed it. When Anton van Leeuwenhoek discovered microbes under his microscope, no one had an explanation for how they got into the water. So it seemed likely that the water must have turned into these animals. Pasteur thought this idea was wrong. He conducted several experiments to make sure.

Pasteur's flask.

The Wellcome Institute Library, London

In a previous series of experiments, Pasteur had learned that certain bacteria made wine spoil. When he heated the wine, the bacteria were killed. (This process of heating to kill bacteria became known as pasteurization.) In another set of experiments, Pasteur heated a flask of water to kill all the bacteria. He took samples of the water and showed under the microscope that the water contained no microbes. He then opened the flasks so that dust could get into the water. He took another sample of the water, looked at it under the microscope, and found bacteria in it. This proved that the bacteria was carried into the water by the dust particles. The bacteria had not grown out of the water.

Once people believed that all living things came only from other living things, it was easier for Pasteur to prove that diseases were caused by living things. While conducting his experiments on wine, Pasteur had wondered if bacteria might also cause diseases in humans.

Pasteur began conducting experiments on animals with anthrax, a disease common in sheep and cattle. While looking under the microscope at blood samples from the sick animals, Pasteur discovered bacteria that were common to all of the infected animals. He knew that if he could inject healthy animals with this bacteria, and they got anthrax, it would prove that the bacteria caused the disease. Pasteur injected healthy rabbits and guinea pigs with a solution that contained the bacteria. All the animals became sick and died, proving the bacteria caused the disease. Using this information, Pasteur was able to develop a vaccine for anthrax.

FIGHTING GERMS

Pasteur's work made people aware that bacteria, or germs, caused diseases and infections. Joseph Lister, a Scottish surgeon who was a friend of Pasteur's, began to sterilize all his equipment before an operation to get rid of germs. He made sure that only clean gloves were used by his assistants. He disinfected wounds with carbolic acid to kill germs. Sure enough, his patients rarely died of infections, and other surgeons began to use his methods.

Although doctors could take steps to prevent germs on the outside of the body from spreading or infecting people, they had no way to kill the germs once they were inside the body. This important step in fighting diseases took place less than fifty years ago when Alexander Fleming discovered a substance that would kill bacteria. Quite by accident, Fleming noticed that one of his lab experiments on bacteria was contaminated with mold. Instead of just throwing the ruined experiment away, Fleming studied it carefully. What he found was extraordinary. The mold destroyed the bacteria. Fleming then tested the

penicillin
Pfizer Inc.

mold on other types of bacteria and found it had the same effect on many of them. Years of testing confirmed Fleming's observations. The substance Fleming found was penicillin, modern medicine's first antibiotic. Since its discovery, penicillin has saved hundreds of thousands of lives. Many infections that once killed people are now easily treated.

It is only within the last hundred years that most people in the United States have come to believe that Hippocrates' guesses are true. All medical research now assumes that the human body is part of nature, and that diseases have explanations just like everything else in

A modern-day medical lab.
© SIU Biomedical/Custom Medical Stock Photo

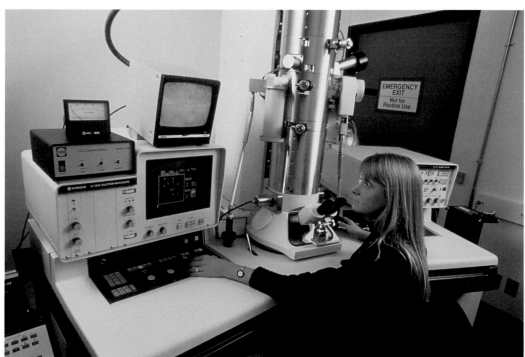

nature. As the natural causes of diseases are discovered, scientists are able to find ways of stopping those diseases. More and more diseases can be prevented or cured. There has been tremendous progress in the last hundred years.

But there is a great deal that we don't know. We still cannot cure many diseases. We don't understand why some people get cancer or heart disease. Millions of people, however, are involved in research on these diseases and on the drugs to cure them. They all accept that Hippocrates was right. But, his idea is still just a guess. And while we think there must be natural causes for these diseases, we don't know what they are. When someone gets cancer today, we are almost as mystified and helpless as people were about any disease a few hundred years ago. If you become a doctor or a medical researcher you may be one of the heroes, like Jenner or Pasteur, who have dispelled some of that fear.

MEET A. W. CARUS, AUTHOR

A.W. Carus is the president of Open Court Publishing Company. When the editors of this book were unable to find a short article surveying the history of medicine for this unit, they asked Carus to write one because they knew he had been trained as a historian. The task was a welcome self-indulgence: "Writing is hard, but it's satisfying to get something down on paper. Running a company never gives you a sense of completion like that."

FINE ART
MEDICINE

Acupuncture figure.
c. 1880. Japanese.

Papier-mâché. Peabody Museum
of Salem. E22.555

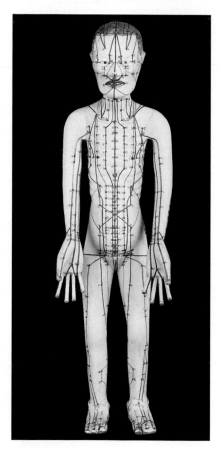

Oath-taking and healing figure
(Nkisi N' Kondi). Late 19th century.
Yombe people, Zaire.

Wood, iron, fiber, paint, cowrie shell, and clay. Field
Museum of Natural History, Chicago. A109327

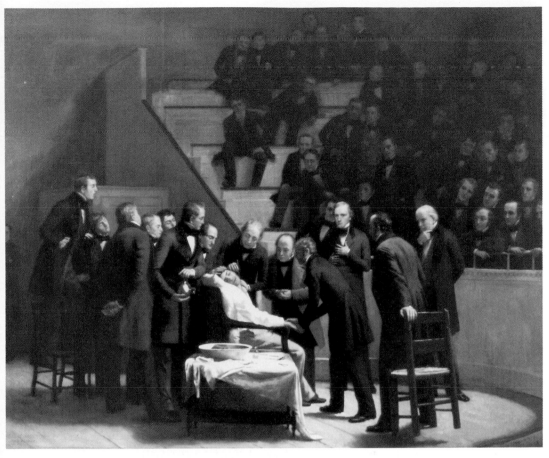

First Operation Under Ether. 1882. Robert Hinckley.

Oil on canvas. Francis A. Countway Library Collection, Boston Medical Library

Women in medicine.
13th century.

Latin manuscript illustration.
Bibliothèque Nationale, Paris

THE BRIDGE DANCERS

Carol Saller
illustrated by
Gerald Talifero

Mama gives the comb a yank through the mess of Callie's long, wild hair, and Callie gives a yell like you've never heard before. That's not to say I've never heard it before; I've heard it plenty. Callie says when she grows up she's going to the city to live, where she'll start a new style. All the ladies will come to her and pay a lot of money to get their hair tangled up in knots, and she'll get rich and never comb her hair again.

I'm not a lot like Callie. My hair doesn't fly around much, and I like it combed, and I don't often think about leaving this mountain. Callie's going to be thirteen soon. I'm only eleven, and I've never even been across the bridge.

When Callie's all combed, we go down the path to the bridge. It's our favorite place to play when our chores are done. The dirt path is steep from our house down the twisty old hill. We like to run down fast, bouncing off the little trees in a crazy zigzag, but when we reach the edge of the gorge, the path levels off and we run alongside it. To folks way down below on the river we must look like two little pokeberries, up high on the mountain's edge.

What we call the bridge isn't the real bridge, where horses and buggies can get across, that's a few miles off along the path. Our bridge is just a shaky old skeleton, a tangle of ropes and boards that ripples and swings in the breeze. Our house is the closest one to this bridge. The next nearest is

the Ketchums' place, another mile up the mountain. Most of our neighbors live across the gorge; Mama says there are seven houses within the first half hour's walk. Mama often has to cross the bridge, but we're not allowed.

On this day, the wind is strong and the bridge is rocking like a boat in a storm. We make clover chains and toss them into the gorge, watching them blow away and then down, down. We count the seconds till they hit the water far below. Callie stays by the edge, but I spy some yellow-eyed daisies growing up the hill a ways, and I know Mama will want them. If you boil daisies—stalks, leaves, and all—it makes a tea that's good for coughs, or a lotion for bruises and sores. Mama doctors most of the folks on this mountain, and we always keep a store of dried plants for medicine. I pull the best ones and put them in my apron pocket.

Later, when the sun is behind the mountain and I'm getting cold and hungry, I start back up the path, but Callie doesn't want to go. "Maisie! I dare you to stand on the bridge!" she calls, just like she does every time we're here. I don't answer, but I stop and turn to look. She knows the thought of it scares me.

Now she skips up the hill a little ways and stands on her toes like a dancer, her skirt ballooning in the wind. In the gloomy light of sundown she is ghostlike and beautiful. "Announcing . . . Calpurnia the Great!" She twirls and leaps and strikes a pose with one toe pointed forward: "Calpurnia—the Daring Bridge Dancer!"

I laugh. I'm pretty sure she's only teasing. Callie dances toward the bridge, humming a tune that she imagines sounds like a circus. When she gets to the part of the bridge that sits on land, she holds on to one post and points her foot out toward the gorge, leaning back in a swoop. Then she grabs both posts and slides both feet out onto the bridge. She starts to slip, but before I can cry out, she turns back, laughing. My heart is jumping. I'm getting ready to run and pull her away from the bridge when she skips aside quick as lightning and starts chewing a piece of clover. In a second I see why.

Mama is huffing down the path. She's lugging her doctoring bag and has to watch her step. If she'd seen Callie fooling around on the bridge we'd both have caught it. "Girls, I've got to attend to Mrs. Gainie," Mama says, putting her bag down for a rest. "She thought the baby would come last night, but tonight's the full moon. It'll come tonight." She looks us over and frowns across the gorge. "I might be gone till sunup, so get yourselves some supper, and don't forget to bolt the door, you hear?" She points at some dark clouds moving fast across the sky. "Hurry on up. I've already made a fire—there's a storm blowing." We nod. She starts for the bridge.

"Mama?" I call, and she stops and turns. "Is Mrs. Gainie going to be all right?" Mama nods. "She's a strong woman." She reaches for the bridge rail with one hand.

"Wait!" I call.

Mama stops again. "What is it, Maisie?"

"Have you got the tansy I picked?" I ask. Tansy is supposed to help a baby come, but if it doesn't do that, at least it keeps the bugs away.

Mama says, "I've got it, but I don't expect to need it this time." She smiles at me. "I'll mind my steps on the bridge, Maisie." Mama knows I'm afraid.

When Mama crosses the bridge, I never let go of her with my eyes. She's a big, heavy woman, and when she steps off the land part, the whole bridge from one side to the other dips into a sharp V with Mama at the bottom point. She goes slow, holding the ropes with one hand and her bag with the other, and she walks in a careful rhythm, giving the bridge time to bounce just right between steps. Callie says, "She won't fall if you look away," but I never look away. On the other side it's already dark, but we can just see Mama turn and wave. We wave back, and Mama disappears around the side of the mountain down the path to the Gainies'.

"Come on, Callie," I say, starting up the path. I know that there's supper to get and more wood to gather and plenty else to do. But Callie isn't of a mind to work. She throws her blade of grass to the wind and runs ahead of me, her arms flung wide. "Burst into jubilant song!" she cries. "The everlasting chains are loosed and we are free!" Callie gets a lot of big words from reading the Bible. "Let us soar into the heavens, never to be enchained again!"

With that, she scampers off the path into the brush, and is soon just a flutter of white in the dusk, dancing and dodging among the trees. I feel the first drops of rain, and in a moment Callie is back.

"Maisie, I know what let's do," she says, blocking the path. She has to raise her voice now against the wind.

"What?" I ask with a frown. Callie's smile looks like it's hiding a bad idea, and I'm not sure I want to know.

"Let's get the ax and split a log for the fire," she says, wrapping her skirt around her and skipping along beside me. "There's a big storm. Let's have a fire that will last us all night."

I'm not sure. A fire would be good on a cold, stormy night, and I know there's only kindling left in the box. But Mama's the one who chops the wood. She takes down that big old ax from its pegs high on the wall and tells us to stand away. She's never told us not to touch it, but I have a feeling that we're not supposed to. I shake my head. "Callie, I don't hardly think you could even lift that ax. You're likely to get yourself killed." But my words blow away with the wind, and Callie is already halfway up to the house. I start to run, too, but I've never yet stopped Callie from doing what she wants to do. I figure the best I can do is be there when she needs help.

When I get to the door, Callie has the lantern lit and is dragging the rocking chair over to the wall. "Don't stand on that—it's too tottery!" I cry, and I run to hold the rocker while Callie climbs up and waits for the wobbling to stop. When the chair is still, she reaches up both hands to lift the ax from its pegs. It's heavy, all right; I can see by the way Callie's muscles stand out on her arms. Just when she's got it lifted off the pegs, the wind blows the door shut with a powerful "bang!" and we both jump with fright. The rocker pitches, and Callie falls.

For a long moment it seems like nothing happens. My thoughts stop; even my heart seems to stop. Then Callie is

crying out with pain and fear. It's her leg, cut deep by the ax. She clutches hold of my arm, tight, and gasps with the force of the pain. "Maisie, hurry and get Mama!" she whispers. "Callie . . ." I start to say, thinking about the wind, the dark, the bridge. Callie sees how I don't want to go, and she looks at me, begging with her eyes. "Maisie, I'm sorry—but you've got to go! You're the only one who can help me!"

I don't want to think about what Callie is saying. Instead I grab one of the clean cloths Mama uses for straining her herb medicines, and with shaky fingers, tie it tight around

Callie's leg. I take a quilt from the bed and put it over her, then run to the kindling pile and throw an armload of sticks on the fire. Callie is crying; the wind is crying. I light another lantern and wonder how I can cross the bridge, in the night, in the storm.

Outside, the wind and trees are whipping at the sky. I hold my skirt in one hand, the lantern in the other, and stumble in the quivery light down the path to the bridge. With my whole heart I wish there was some other way to fetch Mama. I think of Mama with her jars and packets, her sure hands and her healing ways. She'll stop the bleeding with a poultice of yarrow; she'll make an herb tea that will help Callie sleep. But Mama is far across the valley—how will I ever cross that bridge . . . Near the bottom of the hill, I can hear it before I see it, ropes groaning and boards creaking, as it tosses in the storm.

I stand at the edge of the gorge, my lantern lighting the first few steps of the rain-slicked bridge. The fear in me is so powerful it stings my eyes, and I know I don't have the courage for even the first step. But I remember what Callie said—"Maisie, you're the only one who can help me"—and I step onto the bridge with both feet.

The bridge pitches and plunges. I grab for the ropes, and the lantern flies from my hands. "No!" I shriek, as it rolls away and drops into the darkness. On my hands and knees, I crawl back to the edge of the gorge, sobbing in the terrible black night, crying for Callie, crying for Mama. How can I cross the bridge . . . how can I help Callie . . . think what to do, Maisie, think what to do. With my face near the ground, I make myself take slow breaths. I can smell clover, damp with rain.

Suddenly, I know what to do. I pick myself up and start back up the path, feeling my way in the darkness, guided by the small light in the house at the top of the hill. I remember all the times I've watched Mama with her bag, with her poke leaves for burns, her chickweed for tummyache. It's the yarrow plant that stops someone bleeding, and I can make the poultice myself. Near the top I begin to run.

When I burst in through the door, I see that Callie's face is pale. "Maisie—Mama!" she says, weakly. "There, Callie, don't fret; it's going to be fine," I comfort her. "I know what to do. Mama will come later, but I know just what to do."

My hands shake a little as I set the kettle on to boil—the fire is still burning strong. Then I go to Mama's cupboard of crushed and dried plants. I find some yarrow and wrap it in a clean muslin cloth to make the poultice. My fingers are sure now—Mama does it exactly so. Then I take a handful of dried feverfew and put it in a pot, for tea. Callie is moaning, so I sit by her and talk. "Yarrow is just the thing—and I remember I picked this myself! It has such pretty little flowers, and so many funny names: thousand-leaf, angel flower, bunch-a-daisies, sneezewort. It won't take but a minute, once that water's boiled. Don't you worry, Callie. Maisie can take care of you."

When the water is boiling, I pour some into the teapot with the feverfew and put it near the window to cool. Then

I put the wrapped-up yarrow into the kettle and put the kettle back on the fire—not too long, just long enough for the water to soak in and soften the yarrow. Then I scoop out the poultice with a ladle, and after a minute, while it's still hot, I put it carefully on Callie's leg. I know it will hurt, so I keep talking. "Listen to that rain! It's really starting to pour now. You know, this is a pretty bad cut, Callie, and it hasn't stopped bleeding yet. This poultice will stop it. Can you smell how sweet?" But Callie yells when the poultice touches her leg.

When the tea is cool, I pour some into a cup, and hold up Callie's head for her to drink. "That's good," I tell her. "This will ease the pain. Maybe you can sleep a little; sleep

till Mama comes." I rest her head in my lap, leaning my back against the wall. Rain thrashes the roof as I stroke her hair, all tangled and wild. I talk on and on, about ox-eye daisies and Queen Anne's lace, chickweed and tansy, the names like song words, lulling her to sleep at last.

When Mama came home early the next morning, she found us sleeping on the floor. She unwrapped the cloths and washed out the cut—Callie hollered like anything—and said I'd done just what she'd have done herself. She never scolded about the ax—she knew there was no need—but she did ask why I hadn't come to fetch her. I was ashamed, telling Mama how I'd been too afraid to cross the bridge. "You've got good sense, Maisie," she answered. "I guess there's more than one way to cross a bridge."

It's been three months since Callie was hurt, and she's healed as much as she ever will. There's a fearsome scar on her leg, but Callie says that when she goes to live in the city she'll wear long pants like the men and no one will ever know.

Ever since I took care of Callie, Mama has let me help her with the doctoring. From the time I was little, I've helped her find and dry the flowers, but now I go along and watch when she tends to sick folks. When Callie talks about the city, I sometimes think I might visit her there. But for me, I think the mountain will always be my home. I like the way the mountain needs Mama. Someday I think it's going to need me, too.

THE NEW DOCTOR

from YOU CAN HEAR A MAGPIE SMILE
by Paula G. Paul
illustrated by Jim Cummins

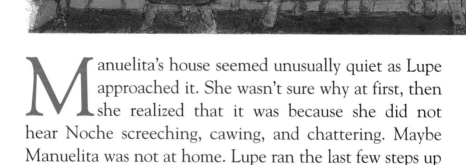

anuelita's house seemed unusually quiet as Lupe approached it. She wasn't sure why at first, then she realized that it was because she did not hear Noche screeching, cawing, and chattering. Maybe Manuelita was not at home. Lupe ran the last few steps up to the front and knocked on the door.

Still no sounds came from inside the house, but soon the door opened noiselessly, and Lupe saw Manuelita standing in front of her. Noche was perched on her shoulder, his long tail hanging down her back. Manuelita said nothing, but stepped aside for Lupe to enter.

"I thought you weren't home," Lupe said.

"In a few more ticks of the clock, we would not have been," Manuelita said.

As Lupe walked into the kitchen, she saw several small cloth bags lying on the table and a large knapsack beside them. Manuelita began gathering up the bags and putting them inside the knapsack.

"You are going to gather herbs," Lupe said. She had seen Manuelita make these preparations before.

Manuelita nodded. She turned toward the cupboard to check the contents of a glass jar. Noche almost lost his balance with the turn and fluttered his wings to keep his position on Manuelita's shoulder. He seemed to know that

Manuelita was going out and was making sure he stuck close beside her so that she would not leave him behind.

"You will look for summer herbs along the river? May I go with you?" Lupe asked eagerly.

"No," Manuelita answered. "I am going into the mountains."

"The mountains?" Lupe asked puzzled. There was a bigger variety of herbs along the river than in the mountains.

"Yes," Manuelita answered. "I will need more osha."

"But I just brought you some. Remember? I gathered it when Maria and I were lost, and—"

"Yes," Manuelita said. "But I will need more. Much more. There is nowhere else in the whole country that osha is as plentiful and as strong as it is in these mountains here."

Lupe wondered why Manuelita thought she would need so much of the herb. She thought of all the things it was used for. The root could be boiled for upset stomach and headaches, or ground to a powder and mixed with flour to paste on the chest of someone who had a cold, or placed on a sore spot on the body to aid healing. The green leaves could be cooked with meat or beans and eaten regularly, just to stay healthy.

Maybe Manuelita thought there was going to be a lot of sickness in the village. But with the new doctor's popularity, many people would no doubt go to her with their complaints. Manuelita must know that, too. It didn't make sense.

Oh, well, Lupe thought, at least Manuelita doesn't seem unhappy. She is still going about her work as usual. She is being her old dependable self. Maybe that is a good sign.

Still, Lupe wanted to be with her friend.

"I will go with you into the mountains," she said. "I will have to ask Mama, of course, but I'm sure if she knows you are going, she will—"

"No." Manuelita's voice was firm. "I must go alone."

"But—"

Manuelita reached toward Lupe and held her shoulders. "I will go alone," she said, looking deep into Lupe's eyes, "but when I come back, you must come to me."

Lupe searched Manuelita's face, trying to understand. "Yes, of course, I will come," she said.

"Then go and play now. There is still time for that."

Lupe thought that was a strange thing for Manuelita to say, but Manuelita said many strange things. She didn't have time to ask her about it, however, because Manuelita had finished packing her knapsack and was ushering her out the door.

As Lupe started through the brush toward the village, she looked back to see Manuelita, carrying the knapsack and with Noche clinging to her shoulder. The bird was not making a sound but was acting as if he dared not be naughty for fear he would be left behind.

By the time Lupe reached the village, her friend Maria had found someone else to play hopscotch with her. They were too far along with the game to add a newcomer, so

Lupe walked away from the sandy spot, looking for something else to do.

She walked past the school and saw several children on the playground, but she didn't feel like joining them. She just kept walking, and before she realized it, she found herself in front of the new temporary clinic building.

There didn't seem to be any cars around it, and the only activity going on was at the noisy construction site for the permanent building nearby. Lupe decided to walk up to the temporary building and peek inside for another look. Since the front door was open just a crack, she tried to see through it. At first, she couldn't see too clearly, so she leaned closer to the door. Just as she did, the door opened from the inside, and Lupe tumbled forward, sprawling on the floor and looking at a pair of sandals. The feet inside the sandals were webbed by gossamer-thin nylon hose.

"Well, what have we here?" said a voice from above. Lupe looked up and saw that both the feet and the voice belonged to Dr. Johnson. The doctor came down to her knees and looked at Lupe. "Are you hurt?" she asked.

"No!" Lupe said. She jumped up quickly and dusted herself off.

"I didn't mean to make you fall. I opened the door to get a breath of fresh air, and I had no idea you were leaning against it."

Lupe ducked her head to hide her burning cheeks.

"Oh, look," the doctor said. "You've scraped your knee on the threshold. Let's see what we can do about that."

Dr. Johnson led Lupe into the examination room. She took her to the sink and washed the knee with warm soapy water, then rinsed and dried it. Next, she took a bottle of red liquid from a shelf and dabbed some of the liquid on the scraped spot. The red medicine caused Lupe's knee to burn furiously, but she did not cry out, and she swallowed hard to keep the tears from her eyes.

The treatment was very much the same as Manuelita would have given. She would have washed the area and dried it. Sometimes she even used the fiery red medicine you could buy at the grocery store, but more often, she would dab on a plaster made from the osha.

"There," Dr. Johnson said, putting the bottle of medicine away. "You have been my first patient, and you have come even before the clinic is officially open. It is to open tomorrow, you know. And I've spent all day today try-ing to get things organized and put away." The doctor sat down at her desk and faced Lupe. She smiled and said, "Now tell me, what can I do for you? Did you come for something special?"

"Nothing special," Lupe said, her voice very low.

"Perhaps you were just curious."

Lupe nodded her head.

"I can understand," Dr. Johnson said. "You have never had a clinic here before, and I suppose you wanted to see what it is like. I would have been the same way at your age. I was curious about just about everything—always poking my nose into something, and often getting into trouble."

Lupe looked up at the doctor, surprised. She was trying to imagine her as a little girl, poking her nose into things. The doctor was laughing at her memories, and the short curls on her head bounced as she laughed. Lupe found herself laughing with her.

"What is your name?" Dr. Johnson asked.

"Lupe Montano."

"I'm Dr. Eleanor Johnson. Did I meet you at the reception? I'm sorry I don't remember, but there were a lot of people there."

Lupe shook her head. "I wasn't there," she said. Lupe let her eyes roam around the room. Dr. Johnson had placed many things on the shelves and counters. There were bottles and jars which Lupe thought must contain medicines, but she didn't know what all the strange-looking tools were for.

"What are those for?" Lupe heard herself asking. She was surprised at her own question. She hadn't meant to ask anything, but her curiosity was stronger than her shyness.

"This?" Dr. Johnson asked, picking up a piece of cloth attached to ropes and dials. "This is for taking blood pressure. Look, I'll show you how it works." The doctor wrapped the cloth around Lupe's arm. She put something in her own ears and placed the end of it to Lupe's arm also.

"When I listen here" —Dr. Johnson pointed to the thing in her ears— "and look at this" she pointed to the

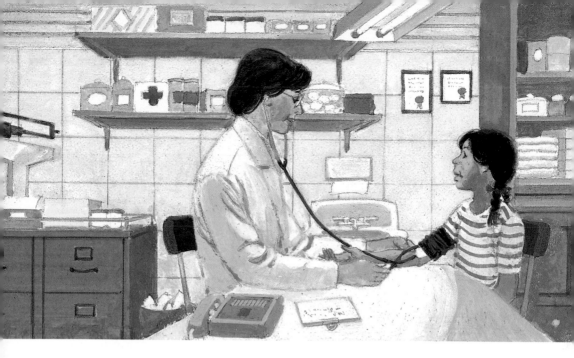

dial— "it helps me find out a little about your body, and maybe whether you are well or sick."

"What do you hear with that?" Lupe asked, pointing to the thing in the doctor's ears.

"This is a stethoscope, and I can hear your heartbeat," the doctor said, and she let Lupe listen to her own heartbeat.

"We will also have X rays, and on certain days of the week, we will have people come here to help me with them. An X ray takes pictures of the inside of your body."

Lupe had heard about X rays in school, although she had never seen one. Taking a picture, from the outside, of the inside of a person's body seemed more like witchcraft to her than anything Manuelita had ever done.

She looked up at the shelves full of bottles. "You have many remedies," she said. "It must have taken you a long time to mix them all."

"Oh, I didn't make them myself." The doctor laughed.

"Then where did you get them?" Lupe asked.

"Why, I bought them, from companies that sell medicines. There are many companies that know how to make medicines much better than I could."

Lupe looked at her silently. She wondered how she knew the medicines were good if she did not make them herself.

"I'll have a lot of advantages to share with you," Dr. Johnson said. "You won't have to travel all the way to Albuquerque when you are sick, or rely on home remedies you make yourself, that don't work most of the time. I'm looking forward to bringing that to all of you, and I'm looking forward to being your friend."

Dr. Johnson reached her hand toward Lupe's, but Lupe pulled her hand away and jumped up from her chair.

"I've got to go now," she said. "I forgot to tell my mother where I would be."

Lupe ran out of the building and down the road toward her house. She did not want to be friends with the new doctor, because the new doctor could not be Manuelita's friend. The new doctor would not want to have anything to do with a person who mixed her own medicines and did not know how to take pictures of people's insides.

Manuelita was gone for several days. Lupe began to worry about her. Manuelita had gone out searching for herbs and stayed far into the night and even overnight before, but never had she been gone this long. Lupe was also concerned because so many people had been going to the clinic. She was afraid they had abandoned Manuelita completely.

Worst of all, Lupe felt disloyal and guilty about the amount of time she, herself, had spent at the new clinic. She couldn't seem to help herself, though. She was fascinated by all the new medicines and strange instruments and, although she did not like to admit it, by the new doctor herself.

One day, when she couldn't talk Maria into going with her, Lupe decided to walk over to the clinic alone. She told herself she only wanted to see how the new building was coming along and perhaps catch a glimpse of Alonzo working with the big machines she'd heard him talk about. But before long, she was seated on the ground in front of the temporary mobile-home clinic, watching people coming and going. Occasionally, if it was someone she knew well enough, she would ask what their ailment was before they went in and what the treatment had been as they came out.

Manuelita had been right. The new doctor's medicine was often very different from hers.

Finally, when the sun was quite low on the horizon, Dr. Johnson herself came to the door. She took off her white coat and held it across her arm. She was wearing a summer dress made of a pretty blue material. It looked nice with her sandals.

"Hello, Lupe," she said. "Someone told me you were out here. Would you like to come in?"

Lupe shook her head.

"Oh, you needn't be shy," Dr. Johnson said. "You seem to be very interested in medicine. Wouldn't you like to talk? I enjoy talking to you."

"It's getting late. It will soon be time for supper," Lupe said, and she ran toward home.

The next time Lupe saw the doctor was in the grocery store. Lupe had gone there to get some flour for her mother to make *tortillas*. A few of the village men were standing around inside the store talking, and Dr. Johnson was talking to Mr. Baca, the owner of the store. She held a can of something in her hand and read the label.

"I don't know," she said. "I do hate to use this. I don't like these poisons, but the bugs are getting to be a problem at the clinic, and I've got to do something."

"You could try calabasilla leaves," Lupe blurted out.

"What?" Dr. Johnson turned around with a surprised look on her face. "Oh, hello, Lupe. I didn't know you were here. Seems you're always surprising me."

"I can bring you some leaves," Lupe said.

"Some what?"

"Leaves. Dried calabasilla leaves. If you sprinkle them around the edges of the rooms, it will keep the bugs out."

"Really? I've never heard of that."

"Works good," said one of the villagers in the store.

"Sure does," said another.

"Lupe knows," said still another.

"I'll bring you some tomorrow," Lupe said. She put the money for the flour on the counter.

Dr. Johnson had a funny look on her face, as if she didn't believe the dried leaves would work. But if she said anything in reply, Lupe didn't hear her over the noise of Mr. Baca's ancient cash register.

Lupe walked out of the store as quickly as she could. She would go back to the clinic just one more time, to deliver the leaves, she told herself. That would be her way of repaying Dr. Johnson for fixing her scraped knee. Every time

Lupe thought of that incident, her heart sank. What would Manuelita think if she ever found out that her friend, Lupe Montano, had been the new doctor's first patient!

The day after Lupe had seen Dr. Johnson in the grocery store, she and Maria went down to the sandy spot to play hopscotch. While they were playing, Lupe heard a familiar cawing sound and looked up to see Manuelita walking through the brush toward her house. Noche, as usual, was perched on her shoulder.

"Manuelita's back!" Lupe said to Maria.

"Are you going to stop the game and go see her?" Maria asked, sounding disappointed.

"No," Lupe said. She stood on one foot and bent to pick up her pebble, then hopped to the end of the series of squares and circles. No matter how glad she was that Manuelita was back, she knew she wouldn't have time to go see her. It was getting late, and she still had to take the calabasilla leaves to Dr. Johnson.

When the game was over, Lupe went home to get the dried leaves. Maybe the doctor doesn't really want them, Lupe thought. She certainly didn't act as if she were anxious to have them. But Lupe was anxious to show her how well they worked, so she went to the pantry and took a jar from a shelf. It was too bad, she thought, to take the last jar, and one that Manuelita had given her family at that. But Lupe knew she could always gather the leaves from the sprawling gourd vines herself, when she found the time. They grew profusely along the river and on the mesas.

Lupe told her mother what she planned to do before she left the house.

"That's very nice of you, Lupe," Mama said. "It is always a good thing to welcome a newcomer with a gift."

When Lupe reached the clinic, there was no one in the waiting room. She was glad, because she didn't want to meet anyone who might say something to Manuelita about her being there. That was one of the reasons she had waited so late to come. She was surprised, however, to hear voices coming from inside the office as she walked up to the door. Two men's voices were speaking rapidly and excitedly in Spanish, and Dr. Johnson's voice was pleading in English.

"Please, please," Lupe could hear the doctor say. "Speak more slowly. My Spanish is not good. I can't understand you."

Lupe walked quietly into the office and saw Uncle Pedro and Cousin Josefa's husband.

"Lupe!" Dr. Johnson said as soon as she saw her. "Maybe you can help. Something's wrong, and these two men are too excited to speak English. Can you tell me what they're saying?"

Lupe questioned the men, who answered her in breathless Spanish. Lupe turned to the doctor.

"It is my Cousin Josefa," she said. "They want you to go to her."

"Josefa?" The doctor seemed puzzled for a moment. "Oh, yes. The woman who is going to have a baby!"

"Yes," Lupe answered. "The men say it is time. They are very excited."

"Of course," Dr. Johnson said with a little laugh. She gathered some things into a bag. "I daresay your cousin will be much calmer than these men are. Come on," she said, motioning to the men. "I'll have to go to her. I have no more facilities for delivering a baby in this temporary building than you'll have at home."

The men followed the doctor out to her car, and everyone, including Lupe, got in. No one seemed to expect Lupe not to go, and she certainly hated to miss the excitement. Maybe it was a good thing she did go along, she decided. She was the one who had to direct the doctor to her cousin's house.

When they arrived, the men took the doctor by one arm each and led her into the house. Cousin Josefa was in a bedroom near the front of the house. Lupe waited in the living room with the family while Dr. Johnson went inside to examine Josefa. That was exactly as Manuelita would have done it, Lupe thought. Soon, the doctor came out of the bedroom. She was smiling.

"Josefa is in fine shape," she said. "It will only be a short wait before the baby is born."

In a little while, Dr. Johnson went back to see about Josefa again.

"She is doing very well," the doctor said when she came out of the bedroom, but her smile had vanished.

The next time the doctor went in to examine Josefa, she looked even more concerned when she emerged.

"She is doing very well, physically, but something is making her unhappy. She kept asking for someone named Manuelita. Is that her friend? Or perhaps her mother?"

"I can get her for you," Lupe said quickly.

"No! No!" said Uncle Pedro.

Just then Josefa called from the bedroom. "Is that Lupe's voice I hear? Let me talk to her."

Dr. Johnson turned to Lupe. "I don't know," she said. "You really shouldn't. . . ."

"Lupe! Let me talk to Lupe!" Josefa called.

Dr. Johnson's brow wrinkled into a frown. She bit her lower lip. "Oh . . . very well," she said. "Come with me." She led Lupe into the bedroom.

"Lupe!" Cousin Josefa said happily from her bed. "The little curandera." She spoke to Lupe softly in Spanish. She could also speak English very well, as could her husband and Uncle Pedro, but, as with most people in the village, when she was excited or had something very special to say, Spanish seemed the best language for saying it. When she had finished talking, Lupe turned to the doctor and told her what Cousin Josefa had said.

"Josefa says that her father, my Uncle Pedro, wants you to help with the baby because he thinks only the new modern ways are good enough for his grandchild, but she says she wants Manuelita to help her, because she is sure Manuelita knows all the right things to do. She says perhaps you know too, but with Manuelita she is certain."

"Who is Manuelita?"

"A curandera."

"A what?"

"A curandera."

"Oh, yes," Dr. Johnson said. "I seem to remember . . . a healer. Yes, I've heard of them. Sometimes associated with witchcraft, aren't they? No, I won't have that."

"Manuelita does not use witchcraft," Lupe said. "That is what Uncle Pedro thinks, but it is not true."

Josefa, who had heard the conversation, began to cry.

"Now, now," Dr. Johnson said, turning to her. "You mustn't be upset."

"I have seen that your kind of medicine is good, but Manuelita's is good, too," Lupe said. "Perhaps you could learn from each other."

"Superstition has no place at a time like this," Dr. Johnson answered.

Josefa was crying softly. "Lupe is a little curandera," she said in English. "She knows the good way."

"You, a curandera?" Dr. Johnson asked. "What does she mean?"

"Manuelita has taught me many things," Lupe said.

"Well, I guess that explains your interest in medicine. Lupe, I welcome you to come talk to me as often as we can find the time. Maybe I can undo some of the wrong ideas you may have."

"But—" Lupe started to protest.

"We don't have time to talk about it now," Dr. Johnson said. "Josefa's baby will be here soon."

Josefa was still crying. "It is only that I want the best for my baby," she said.

"The best thing for you and the baby both is for you to remain calm."

But Josefa only cried harder and clutched at her middle. Dr. Johnson spoke as if she were talking to herself. "She was handling it so well at first."

"Maybe Manuelita could at least help you," Lupe insisted.

"I could use some help," Dr. Johnson said, "but a curandera . . . no." She looked again at the sobbing Josefa.

Dr. Johnson's not going to give in, Lupe thought. She watched as the doctor fussed around Josefa, holding her hand and talking to her softly.

"It's not going to be a good birth if she is so upset," Dr. Johnson said to no one in particular. She turned to Lupe. "Maybe it wouldn't hurt anything for this, this Manuelita just to be here. . . . All right, Lupe, go get the healer."

Lupe ran from the house as fast as she could, still clutching the jar of calabasilla leaves she had forgotten to give to Dr. Johnson. She was breathless when she reached Manuelita's house, but she managed to explain what was happening and to tell her that the new doctor was with Josefa.

She was surprised at how fast the elderly Manuelita was able to get to Josefa's home. Noche flew ahead, circling and returning to Manuelita and Lupe, screeching and talking nonsense. As usual, he was left outside when Manuelita entered the patient's house.

Uncle Pedro stood up to protest as soon as he saw Manuelita.

"What's she doing here?" he asked.

Manuelita did not look at Uncle Pedro, or speak to him. He tried to follow Manuelita into the bedroom, but she slammed the door in his face, almost catching his nose between the door and the wall.

Lupe could hear many noises coming from the bedroom while she waited in the living room with the men.

"The doctor will see that it is done right," Uncle Pedro said, over and over again, to reassure both himself and his son-in-law.

The noises in the bedroom ceased. The silence was brief, interrupted by the cry of a tiny voice. Both of the men jumped from their seats. Dr. Johnson opened the bedroom door.

"Josefa and her husband have a beautiful daughter," she said.

She let everyone go into the room for a few minutes to see Josefa. First Josefa's husband went in, then Uncle Pedro, then Lupe.

Lupe saw Cousin Josefa holding her baby and smiling, and Manuelita standing beside them. Dr. Johnson walked toward Manuelita and held out her hand.

"Thank you," the doctor said. "I . . . I guess I have a lot to learn."

Manuelita took the doctor's hand in hers, but she did not speak.

THE STORY
OF SUSAN
LA FLESCHE
PICOTTE

from HOMEWARD THE ARROW'S FLIGHT
by Marion Marsh Brown
illustrated by Allen Eitzen

Dr. Susan La Flesche Picotte, 1898.

Medical College of Pennsylvania

Susan La Flesche Picotte was the first female Native-American doctor in the United States. After completing medical school she returned to her home and began work as the doctor at the reservation school. In this excerpt, her first weeks as not only the school doctor but doctor for the whole reservation are told.

Susan wrote a letter of application on the very night that she told Rosalie, her sister, she wanted the position of reservation physician. Then she waited anxiously for a reply.

At last the letter arrived. She tore it open eagerly. "Well, finally," she sighed. She carried it to the kitchen where her mother was preparing supper. "I got the appointment," she said. "I don't get any more money though."

Her mother looked up. "So much more work and no more pay?" she asked.

"That's what the letter says: 'As there are no funds available except for your present salary as physician to the government school, we will be unable to pay any additional monies for your additional services as reservation physician.' Well, anyway I have the title. Now to see what I can do with it."

That same night, the first snow of the winter fell. Susan was soon inundated with a siege of colds, grippe, and pneumonia. It was as if the first snowstorm had been a signal for winter illnesses to attack.

She had laid her plans carefully before entering into her new contract to do two jobs for the price of one. She would spend mornings at the school and make house calls in the afternoons. The only problem, she soon discovered, was that there weren't enough hours in the day.

"I don't know why babies always want to get born in the wee hours of the morning," she said to Rosalie, stopping at her sister's house one day on the way to school. She'd been up since midnight and would not have time to go home before she was due at school. She was glad to have a place to clean up and get a cup of coffee.

"Sue, you can't go on this way," her sister said. "You'll ruin your own health."

Susan sighed. "But what else can I do, Ro?"

It was a bad winter, one of the worst Nebraska had seen in many a year. The north wind blew in icy gusts, finding its way around poorly fitted window frames and under ill-hung doors into the Omahas' houses. Many of the houses were getting old and they had not been kept in repair.

When Susan rode up to one in which a windowpane was out, the hole stuffed carelessly with old rags, anger flared in her. Inside, she knew, lay a child on the verge of pneumonia.

"Tom," she said, when she had entered, "there's no excuse for that." She pointed at the window. "When you get your next allotment, buy a piece of glass and some putty and replace that pane."

"You just like Iron Eye," he said, and Susan detected resentment in his tone. "Always try to tell us how to live."

Susan bit her tongue and went about her task of examining the sick child. Was it hopeless, she wondered, trying to teach them? But her father, Iron Eye, had never given up.

One morning when she started for school, the wind was particularly vicious. Reluctantly, she turned Pie, her horse, into it. When they reached the schoolgrounds, she put him immediately into the shed that was provided for bad days. As she turned to the schoolhouse, she noted that the sky looked ominous. It took all her strength to wrench the door open against the wind. "I think we're going to get snow," she called to Marguerite as she entered.

Marguerite turned back, and Susan saw the worried look on her face. "Oh, dear, I hope not. Charlie's sick again. He has an awful cough, Sue, and he was so hot last night, I know he has fever. And he went out to look after the stock this morning. I was hoping you could go by and see him this afternoon."

"Of course I'll go. A little snow won't stop me," Susan replied with a smile, hoping to cheer her sister.

As the morning progressed, the wind howled and the snow grew heavier. In a moment's lull in her work, Susan glanced out the window and discovered she could no longer see the row of trees that formed a windbreak for the school building. She felt a little tug of concern. Some of the children lived quite a distance from school. Perhaps they should be getting home.

It wasn't long until the teachers were consulting her. "Do you think we should dismiss school? If it keeps this up . . ."

"I think it would be wise to
get the children on their way.
It certainly isn't getting any better."

So an early dismissal was agreed upon.

Susan was helping the teachers bundle the children into
coats and overshoes, tying mufflers over mouths and noses,
and giving instruction to the older ones to keep tight hold
of the hands of younger brothers and sisters, when the outside door burst open and a man stumbled in. He was so
caked with snow that at first she didn't recognize him.

"Dr. Susan!" he cried. "Come quick! My Minnie . . ."

"Oh, it's you, Joe," she said. "Has your wife started labor?"
He nodded. "But she's bad, Doctor. Not like before."

"Come on in and warm up, then go home and put lots of
water on the stove to heat. I'll be along shortly."

Joe didn't linger. As soon as the children were on their
way and she had straightened up her office, Susan sought
out Marguerite. "I'll have to wait to see Charlie until after
I deliver Minnie Whitefeather's baby. Joe says she's having
a bad time, so I may be late."

"All right. Be sure to bundle up," Marguerite said. "It
looks like the storm's getting worse."

"That I will. I always come prepared!" Susan
assured her. She pulled her stocking cap down
over her ears and donned the heavy wool
mittens her mother had knit for her.

"I hope you'll be all right," Marguerite
said. "It's a long way over there."

"Don't worry. You can depend on
Pie!" Susan waved a cheery good bye
and plunged out into the storm. She
had to fight her way to the shed.
Already drifts were piling high. "I
hope the children are all safely home
by now," she thought. Her pony was
nervous. "Good old Pie," she said,
patting the sleek neck as she mount-
ed. "When you were a young one
and we went racing across the hills,

you didn't think you were going to have to plow through all kinds of weather with me when you grew old, did you?"

The Whitefeathers lived on the northernmost edge of the reservation. Susan turned Pie into the road, and he plodded into the storm. "Good boy!" she said encouragingly. But she couldn't hear her words above the violent shrieking of the wind. Nor, shortly, could she tell whether they were following the road; she could only trust Pie.

It seemed to her that the storm grew worse by the minute. Suddenly Pie stopped, turning his head back as if asking Susan what he should do. She tried to wipe the caked snow from her eyes to see what was wrong and found that her fingers were stiff. But she saw Pie's problem. A huge drift lay across their path. "We'll have to go around it, Pie." She pulled him to the left until they reached a point where the drift tapered off. Pie moved around it, and Susan thought, "Now can we find the road again—if we were on the road?" She pulled on the right rein. But she couldn't tell whether they were going north, for now the storm seemed to be swirling around them from all directions.

Soon another drift blocked their way. But this time Pie wallowed through with a strange, swimming motion. How did he know he could get through that one and not the other, she wondered. Suddenly, having maneuvered the drift, the pony stopped.

"Get up, Pie! We have to go on!" she urged. He did not move. She slapped the stiff reins on his neck, but to no avail. She tried kicking his sides with feet she discovered were numb. "We'll freeze to death! Go on!" Still Pie refused to move.

At length she dismounted. If she could walk on her numb feet, perhaps she could lead him. Stumbling, she made her way to Pie's head.

Then she saw, and she caught her breath in terror. For Pie stood with his head directly over a bundle in the snow—a bundle that she knew instantly was a child.

"Oh, my!" she cried. She lifted the bundle into her arms. It was a boy, one of the little ones they had turned out of school to find his way home. "What were we thinking of?" Susan railed at herself. "Jimmy! Jimmy!" she cried, shaking the child. She scooped the snow off his eyelids. He stirred, and then his eyelids lifted. "Jimmy! It's Dr. Sue. You were asleep, Jimmy.

You have to wake up now." She hoisted him in front of her on the pony, and holding him close to give him warmth from her body, she beat on his arms.

The minute she was back in the saddle, Pie moved on. "Pie! Bless you. You probably saved Jimmy's life."

As Pie pressed on, she continued to talk to Jimmy, working on him as she talked—rubbing his hands, cradling his face against her. "We have to warm up your nose," she told him. He began to cry. "You mustn't cry. Your tears will make cakes of ice!"

She strained her eyes ahead, but she could see nothing against the driving snow. She had no idea how long they had been in this frozen white nightmare. Surely if they were going in the right direction, they should have reached the Whitefeathers' by now. "Pie's going to take us to where it's nice and warm," she soothed Jimmy. And to herself she said, "If he doesn't, it's the end of all of us, you and me and him. And maybe Minnie Whitefeather too."

She tried to keep the child awake, finding to her consternation that she herself was growing drowsy. She well knew that to go to sleep was a sure way to freeze to death.

She must have dozed briefly, for she started when Pie suddenly stopped. She roused herself to urge him on. "Get up, Pie! We can't stop now! We have Jimmy!" She beat on his sides, but he refused to move. The snow had again caked her eyelids, and she pawed at it with unfeeling fists. She supposed they'd come to another drift Pie couldn't manipulate.

As she blinked hard to see, she was suddenly aware of a sound that was not born of the storm. Pie had whinnied. She even felt the ripple of his neck. What did it mean?

Then she saw! They were by the side of a building, sheltered from the wind. It was a barn!

"Pie! Pie! You did it!" she cried.

As she tried stiffly to dismount with Jimmy strong arms were supporting her. It was Joe.

"We—so glad you here, Dr. Sue. We afraid you not make it."

"So was I," Susan said. "Please take care of Pie. We wouldn't be here except for him."

Susan did not get to Marguerite and Charlie's that night, but she did deliver a baby girl. Nor did she get to her sister's home for the two days following, for the storm raged on fiercely through the night, wrapping the reservation in a tight white cocoon that could not be penetrated. There was no way to return Jimmy to his home or to let his parents know that he was safe. Susan agonized over this, but there was nothing she could do.

There were two other Whitefeather children, and Susan noticed that they came to have their hands washed before a meal. She noticed other things: the family's clothes were clean, and the blankets on the beds were clean. "You're doing well with your little family," she praised Minnie.

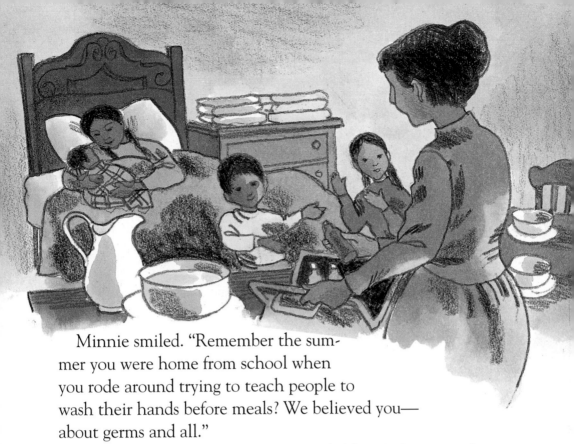

Minnie smiled. "Remember the summer you were home from school when
you rode around trying to teach people to
wash their hands before meals? We believed you—
about germs and all."

"And now you're teaching your children," Susan said
approvingly. "That's fine, Minnie. It means the upcoming
generation will have a better time of it."

When Susan eventually got to Charlie and Marguerite's,
she found Charlie in bed in the throes of a violent chill.
His cough was frightening. She left medicine and tried to
reassure him, but as her sister saw her to the door, she shook
her head. "His lungs are weak, Marg. You'll have to be very
careful."

"I know," Marguerite replied quietly.

"I wonder if she does know," Susan thought as she went
on her snow-clogged way. There was no question in her

mind that he was consumptive, as his mother had been. She had been doing all she could for him, but she feared he would be one she couldn't save—gentle Charlie, who was so good to everyone, especially to Marguerite.

By early February he was continuously confined to his bed, and there was no more Susan could do. Marguerite had to take leave from her teaching position to care for him.

He died quietly, as he had lived, just before the month was out.

"I thought maybe if he could make it till spring . . ." Marguerite said desolately.

"Why don't you come home and live with Mother and me?" Susan suggested. "It would be too lonely for you here."

They sent word of Charlie's death to his family in Dakota, and his brother, Henry, came. "We wanted the family represented at his funeral," he said.

"Henry's different," Susan remarked to Rosalie. "Yet he reminds me of Charlie. Sort of a gayer edition!"

"He's more worldly," Rosalie said.

Susan smiled. It took Ro, who had had less "worldly" exposure than the rest of them, to see straight through to the point. "Yes, you're right," she agreed.

With the funeral over, Henry gone, and Marguerite back in the home where she and Susan had grown up, things settled down into a certain routine. Marguerite went back to teaching, and Susan went on with her doctoring.

"It's like the old days," Susan said one evening when she and Marguerite and their mother sat down to supper.

"Only different," Marguerite said.

"Yes," Susan agreed, thinking of how it had been when Nicomi, her grandmother, and Iron Eye and Rosalie had been at that table. "Things don't stay the same, do they, Mother?"

Her mother shook her head.

"We have to learn to accept change. That was one of the things Father tried to teach us long ago."

Spring was late that year, but when it finally came, it was so beautiful that Susan at times thought she couldn't bear it. Sometimes when she was riding home from a call in early evening, she would dismount and let Pie graze while she gazed down on the greening willows that fringed the river like a band of chartreuse lace. If it weren't too late, she would venture into the woods to look for violets and Dutchman's-breeches and the shy lady's-slipper.

"What a wonderful place to live," she thought. And more and more she could see that her work was bearing fruit. "I'm not accomplishing miracles," she told Rosalie one evening, "but I am beginning to see some of the results of better hygiene and health habits. And we're losing fewer babies and fewer cases to infection."

"You don't need to convince me," Rosalie said. "I can see it on every hand. How pleased Father would be."

SHADOW OF A BULL

Maia Wojciechowska
illustrated by Allen Eitzen

Manolo Olivar is the son of Spain's most famous
bullfighter. Although his father died after being gored by a
bull, Manolo is expected to follow in his father's footsteps.
Everyone expects him to be Spain's next great bullfighter.
But, Manolo lacks afición, *or desire. He knows he does not*
want to be a bullfighter, but he is unsure what he will
become. One day while visiting a fighter who has been gored,
Manolo realizes what he must do.

O n the way to the gored boy's house, Manolo listened to them tell about how bulls can hurt.

"The horn enters cleanly. If only it would exit
that way. But either the man or the bull or both are moving at the time of the goring, and that's why the wounds are
so bad."

"The horn tears into the body, ripping the muscles."

"And there is always the danger of infections. The horn
is dirty, and before penicillin, it was almost always either
amputation or death from infection."

"As far as the bullfighters are concerned, penicillin was
the greatest invention of man."

"Poor devils! When they get gored in small towns there is never a doctor."

"And that's where they usually get gored."

"Even here in Arcangel, there is only one doctor who will touch a horn wound. Only one who knows anything about them, and he is getting old; when he is gone, maybe there will be no one."

"If you must get gored, be sure it's in Madrid."

"In Madrid they have a dozen doctors."

"I knew a doctor once who got rich on bullfighters. And then one day, he took his money and went to a printer and had millions of pamphlets printed. The pamphlet was called 'Stop the National Suicide'."

The men had never said anything before about pain, the amount of it a bullfighter had to endure. And Manolo had never thought before about pain. Now, listening to them, he thought that it would not be of dying that he would be afraid, but of the pain.

'El Magnifico,' lying on sheets that were as white as his face, looked to be about eighteen. The first thing Manolo noticed about him were his lips. They were pale, but he had been biting them. Drops of blood stood out in a row marking the places where the lips had been bitten. Without anyone having to tell him, Manolo knew that the boy was in great pain.

When they came into the room, 'El Magnifico' tried to hide his bloodied lips behind his hand. He did not say much, just that he was feeling all right. When he looked

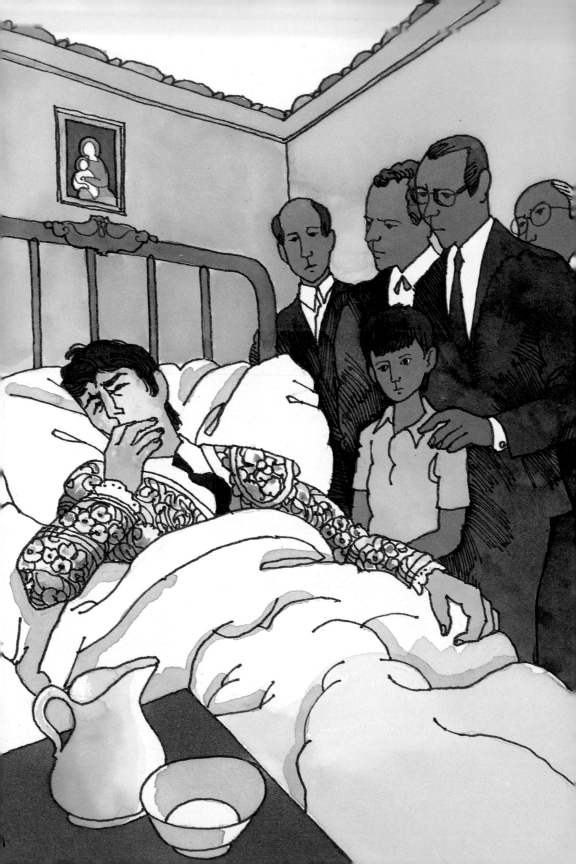

away from the men, he did not look out of the window, but at the wall where there was nothing but a stain. And when he turned back to them, his lips had fresh drops of blood on them.

"I was terrible," the boy said, trying to smile.

"You weren't there long enough," one of the men said, "to let us see how terrible."

"I would have been very bad," 'El Magnifico' said, fighting back tears.

"You might have been fine. It was a good little bull. You were too brave, and sometimes it's silly to be too brave. You don't let the people see how long your courage is, just how wide."

The boy's mother came into the room. She was a big woman with strong hands and a face that seemed carved from a rock.

"The doctor's coming," she said, not looking at the men but looking hard at her son. She waited for him to say something. He said nothing.

"Hasn't the doctor seen you?" one of the men asked.

The boy moaned and coughed to hide the sound of his pain.

"He was out of town," the mother said, looking now at them for the first time, her eyes accusing.

"The barber then, he took care of you in the infirmary?" the man wanted to know.

"Yes," the boy said, "he did the best he could."

"The barber's only a barber," the mother said angrily and left the room.

"He's in great pain. He doesn't show it, but he is in great pain," one of the men said softly to Manolo.

"It never hurts right after the goring. But when it starts hurting, it hurts for a long time," another added.

They heard footsteps outside. They were slow in reaching the door. The doctor was an old man. He shuffled when he moved from the door to the boy's bed. He looked tired. A shock of white hair fell listlessly over his wrinkled forehead as he bent over the boy.

"Olá. How goes it?" He smiled at the boy and passed his hand over the boy's forehead. He did not greet the men, nor did he seem to notice Manolo.

"The barber cleaned it and bound it," the boy said feebly, raising on his elbow and then falling back on the pillows.

The men began to move towards the door.

"Stay," the doctor said not looking at them, taking the light blanket off the boy's bed and reaching into his bag for a pair of scissors. "I want Olivar's son to see what a goring looks like. Come here," he commanded, and Manolo moved closer, his heart beating loudly. "Look!" The doctor had cut the bandage and the gauze and pushed them aside. A flamelike, jagged tear, a foot long and several inches deep ran straight from the boy's knee up his thigh. Manolo caught his breath at the sight of it. "Bend down and look here," the doctor said. "Those are puddles of clotted blood.

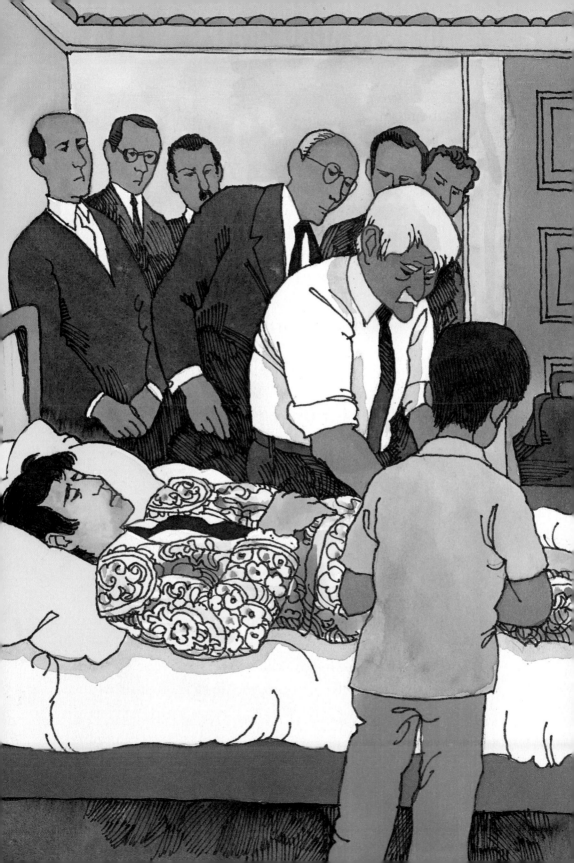

There are about seven different reds beside, all meat. The muscles are purple. The wound is always narrower where the horn enters and wider where it exits. Not pretty, is it?"

Manolo moved away feeling sick; but the voice of the doctor brought him back, and with its sound, so sure and matter of fact, the feeling of sickness left him.

"I'll need your help," the doctor said, still looking at but not touching the wound. "It's a good, clean tear. The barber did his work well. He took the dirt out and cut off the dead flesh."

When he walked to the washbasin, his feet were not shuffling. He scrubbed his hands thoroughly. He put the surgical towel on the bedside table, took some instruments from the bag, put them on the towel, and then reached for a package of gauze pads and put those next to the instruments.

"Hand me those gloves," the doctor said to Manolo, pointing to a pair of rubber gloves in a plastic bag. "Let's see how good a nurse you'd make," he added. "Open the bag without touching the gloves and hold them out to me." Manolo did as he was told.

Manolo watched fascinated, as the doctor's hands moved surely into the wound, exploring the inside of it.

"The horn stayed away from the thigh bone," the doctor said. "He's a lucky boy. What I am doing now," he explained, speaking to Manolo, "is looking for foreign matter; dirt, pieces of horn, or dead flesh. But as I said before, the barber did a very good job of taking all those out of the wound. There is no danger of infection."

The admiration Manolo felt for the doctor was growing with each word, each gesture. No sound came from the pillow. With tenderness the doctor looked away from his work.

"He's fainted," he said with a smile. "Get the bottle of ammonia," he motioned towards the bag, "and a wad of cotton. Moisten the cotton and hold it under his nose."

Again Manolo did as he was told. When he opened the bottle, the strong odor of ammonia invaded his nostrils and spread through the entire room. He bent over the boy and passed the cotton directly under his nose. The boy coughed and jerked his head away.

"Good!" the doctor said watching, "he's not in shock. Just passed out from the pain. He will be fine. What he's got is one of those lucky gorings." His gloved hand pointed to the straight line of the torn flesh, "It's as good a goring as you could wish for, if you were wishing for a good goring. The bad ones are the ones that tear in and change angles. Those are the messy ones, the dangerous ones. But I don't want you to think this is nothing. It's the result of foolishness. Not the beast's, but the man's. The beast is led into the ring, the man walks in himself."

The doctor finished cleaning the wound and then stitched the flesh. Manolo was not asked again to help. He wished the doctor would once more request him to do something. As he watched the magic way the man's hands brought torn flesh together, he thought that what the doctor was doing and had done was the most noble thing a man could do. To bring health back to the sick, to cure the wounded, save the dying. This was what a man should do with his life; this, and not killing bulls.

"It will heal nicely. This one will. But then what?" The doctor walked to the wash basin and began washing the blood off the rubber gloves. "He," he pointed with his head to the boy, "will go on trying to prove that he can be good. And he isn't. But it's a point of honor with him. He will go on trying, and they will give him chances to try because he's fearless and the paying customers know that they will see a goring each time 'El Magnifico' is on the bill. But the tragedy is not that some people are bloodthirsty. The tragedy is that boys like him know of nothing else they want to do. I've grown old looking at wasted lives."

He walked over to Manolo and patted his head.

"The world is a big place," he said gently.

He seemed to want to add something, but he said nothing more. Silently, he put his instruments back in the bag and snapped it shut.

"Thank you for your help," the doctor said to Manolo, but his voice was tired now. The shuffle came back into his steps, and before he reached the door, he looked once again like a very old, very tired, man.

Walking back with the men, Manolo decided that if only he did not have to be a bullfighter he would be a doctor. He wanted to learn how to stop the pain and how to stop the fear of it. If only his father had been a doctor, a famous one, a bullfighters' doctor, then they would expect him to be one, too. And he would study hard. It would not be easy, but he would be learning to do something worthwhile.

He wondered if he were to tell the men, the six men, what he thought he would like to be, if they would listen to him. He looked at the men walking alongside him, talking once again about what they always talked about; and he knew that he would not tell them. He was who he was. A bullfighter's and not a doctor's son, and they expected him to be like his father. Maybe someday he could tell them.

MEET MAIA WOJCIECHOWSKA, AUTHOR

Maia Wojciechowska was born in Poland and has lived in France and the United States. Shadow of a Bull is set in Andalusia, the southern part of Spain. Wojciechowska states: " I have come to love this part of Spain [and] yes, Manolo was a boy there once. He had a face with a long nose and very sad eyes." He looked like a very famous bullfighter in Spain. All the old men of the village thought he reminded them of him too. "I grew very much afraid for him because I thought these old men needed a new hero and, he, the little boy, looked so like their old one. It was through this fear that I thought of the boy as a character for a short story."

THE MICROSCOPE

Maxine Kumin
illustrated by Robert Byrd

Anton Leeuwenhoek was Dutch.
He sold pincushions, cloth, and such.
The waiting townsfolk fumed and fussed
As Anton's dry goods gathered dust.

He worked, instead of tending store,
At grinding special lenses for
A microscope. Some of the things
He looked at were:

mosquitoes' wings,
the hairs of sheep, the legs of lice,
the skin of people, dogs, and mice;
ox eyes, spiders' spinning gear,
fishes' scales, a little smear
of his own blood,

and best of all,
the unknown, busy, very small
bugs that swim and bump and hop
inside a simple water drop.

Impossible! Most Dutchmen said.
This Anton's crazy in the head.
We ought to ship him off to Spain.
He says he's seen a housefly's brain.
He says the water that we drink
Is full of bugs. He's mad, we think!
They call him *Dummkopf*, which means dope.
That's how we got the microscope.

THE GERM
Ogden Nash

A mighty creature is the germ,
Though smaller than the pachyderm.
His customary dwelling place
Is deep within the human race.
His childish pride he often pleases
By giving people strange diseases.
Do you, my poppet, feel infirm?
You probably contain a germ.

SURGEONS MUST BE VERY CAREFUL

Emily Dickinson

Surgeons must be very careful
When they take the knife!
Underneath their fine incisions
Stirs the culprit,—Life!

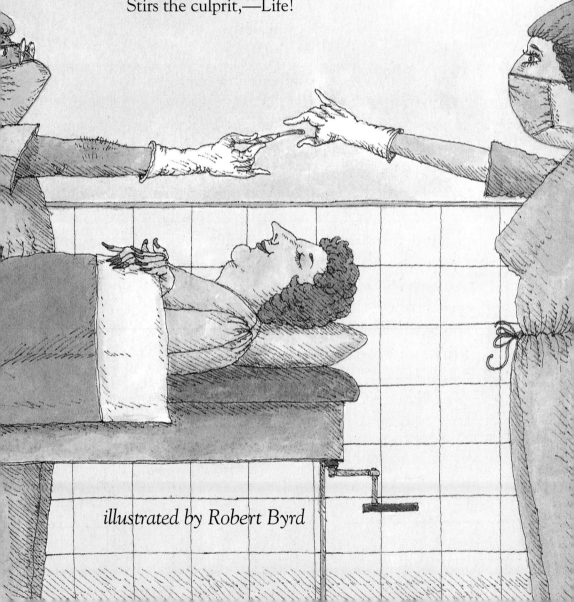

illustrated by Robert Byrd

SEWED UP HIS HEART

from SURE HANDS, STRONG HEART: THE LIFE OF DANIEL HALE WILLIAMS
by Lillie Patterson
illustrated by Leslie Bowman

July 9, 1893, was hot and humid in Chicago. The scorching heat wave wrapped the city like a sweltering blanket and blistered the sidewalks. Rising temperatures sent thermometers zooming toward one hundred degrees.

The heat and high humidity took a heavy toll on young and old, animals and people. Horses pulling carts and streetcars dropped in their tracks. People fainted from heat prostration and sun strokes. No relief was in sight.

Doctors and hospitals were kept busy. The new Provident Hospital was no exception. Dr. Dan kept close watch on his patients. Making his rounds, he looked as immaculate as always, despite the heat. After his late-afternoon rounds were over, he retired to the closet-like room he used for his office.

Suddenly, a young student nurse burst into the room, her long starched skirt rustling as she ran.

"Dr. Dan!" she gasped. "An emergency! We need you."

Without a word Dr. Dan dropped the report he was reading and hurried to the room set aside for emergency cases. The lone hospital intern, Dr. Elmer Barr, came running to assist.

The emergency case was a young man. He had been brought in by his friend, who gave sketchy information. The patient's name: James Cornish. His age: twenty-four years. His occupation: laborer. The illness: he had been stabbed in the chest.

The frightened friend tried to explain what happened. James Cornish had stopped in a neighboring saloon on his way home from work. The heat and a few drinks caused an argument among the customers. A fight broke out. When it ended, Cornish lay on the floor, a knife wound in his chest.

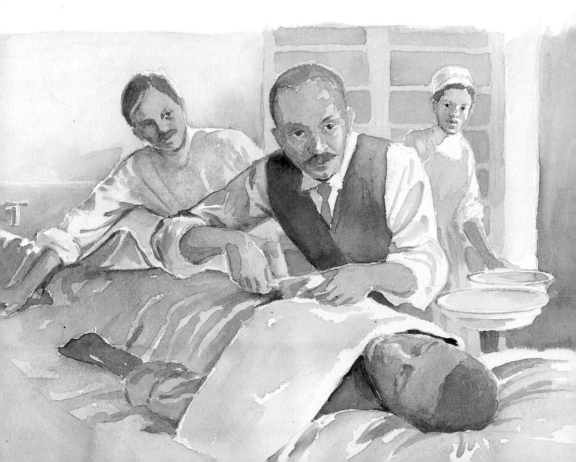

"How long was the knife blade?" Dr. Dan asked as he began his examination. This would give a clue to the depth and seriousness of the wound.

The victim had not seen the knife blade. Nor had his friend. Action in the fight had been too fast and furious.

Dr. Dan discovered that the knife had made an inch-long wound in the chest, just to the left of the breastbone. There was very little external bleeding. Nevertheless, Cornish seemed extremely weak, and his rapid pulse gave cause for concern. The X ray had not yet been invented, so there was no way to determine what was happening inside the chest.

Dr. Dan knew from experience that such cases could develop serious complications. James Cornish must be kept in the hospital, he decided. And he must be watched closely.

That night Dr. Dan slept in the hospital. He did this often when there were serious cases. As he had feared, Cornish's condition worsened during the night. He groaned as severe chest pains stabbed the region above his heart. His breathing became labored. A high pitched cough wracked his sturdy frame. The dark face on the pillow was bathed in perspiration.

Dr. Dan watched the wounded man carefully all night. The next morning, as he took the patient's pulse, he voiced his concern to the intern. "One of the chief blood vessels seems to be damaged," he said to Dr. Barr. The knife must have gone in deep enough to cut the internal

mammary artery, he explained. The heart itself might be damaged.

James Cornish showed symptoms of lapsing into shock.

Both doctors knew that something had to be done, and done quickly. Otherwise Cornish would surely die within a matter of hours.

But what?

The only way to know the damage done would be to open the chest and look inside. In 1893, doctors considered this highly impracticable. For surgery, the chest was still off limits.

Standing beside the patient's bed, the barber-turned-doctor faced the situation squarely. Later he would recall how he weighed the risks of that moment. Thoughts tumbled through his mind as furiously as flurries in a wintry Chicago snowstorm.

He knew that medical experts repeatedly warned against opening the thorax, the segment of the body containing the heart and lungs. Heart wounds were usually considered fatal. As a medical student, Dr. Dan had read a quote from an eminent physician-writer. "Any surgeon who would attempt to suture a wound of the heart," the surgeon wrote, "is not worthy of the serious consideration of his colleagues."

So far, doctors had followed this cautious advice.

The risks were there for him and for Cornish. If he did not attempt an operation, Dr. Dan reasoned, the patient would die. Nobody would blame the doctor. Such cases often died.

On the other hand, if he opened the chest and Cornish died anyway, there would be certain condemnation from medical groups. His reputation as a surgeon would be questioned, perhaps lost.

The odds were against both him and Cornish. But Daniel Hale Williams had never allowed the odds to intimidate him.

Dr. Dan lifted his chin, the way he did when he faced a challenge. The storm of doubts suddenly swept away, leaving his mind clear and calm as a rain-washed April morning.

The surgeon quietly told his decision to the intern. Two words he spoke. "I'll operate."

The word spread quickly through Provident hospital. Like a small army alerted to do battle, student nurses rushed to get the operating room ready and prepare the patient. They knew Dr. Dan's strict rules regarding asepsis, or preventing infection. The instruments, the room, furniture; everything that came in contact with the patient must be free of microbes that might cause infection.

Meanwhile, Dr. Dan sent a hurried message to a few doctors who often came to watch him operate. The intern, a medical student, and four doctors appeared. Dr. George Hall of Provident's staff was there. So was Dr. Dan's friend, Dr. William Morgan. The circle of watchers gathered in the operating room; four white, two black.

Dr. Dan scrubbed his hands and arms thoroughly. Then, with a nod toward his colleagues, he walked over and looked down at Cornish, now under the effects of anesthesia. Strong shafts of sunlight slanted through a window, giving the doctor's curly red hair a glossy luster. His thin, sensitive mouth drew taut with concentration.

The surgical nurse, proud of her training, stood at attention.

Scalpel!

A loud sigh escaped one of the doctors when the light, straight knife touched Cornish's bare skin. After that there was silence from the onlookers.

None of them knew what would happen next. How would the body react when air suddenly hit the chest cavity? Would vital chest organs shift too far out of place? Dr. Dan could not benefit from the experiences of other doctors. No paper had been written, no lectures given to guide him. Dr. Dan was pioneering in an unexplored territory. He was on his own.

The surgeon worked swiftly. He had to. The surgeon of 1893 did not have a variety of anesthetics or artificial airways to keep the patient's windpipe open. Blood transfusion techniques were unknown. Penicillin and other infection-fighting drugs had not been discovered.

Quickly, Dr. Dan made the incision, lengthening the stab wound to the right. Expertly, he cut through the skin and the layers of fat beneath it. Now he could see the breastbone and the ribs. He made another cut to separate the rib cartilage from the sternum.

Long years of studying and teaching human anatomy gave his every movement confidence. Working with precision, he made his way through the network of cartilages, nerves, blood vessels. A few inches from the breastbone he cut through the cartilage to make a little opening, like a trapdoor.

Bending his head close to the patient's chest, he peered through the opening he had made. Now he could examine the internal blood vessels.

Now he could see the heart!

The tough bundle of muscles throbbed and jerked and pulsated, sending food and oxygen through the body. Dr. Dan examined the pericardium, the fibrous sac that protected the pear-shaped heart and allowed it to beat without rubbing against other parts of the body.

At each step, Dr. Dan reported his findings to the group of observers. The vital pericardium was cut—a tear of about an inch and a quarter in length. He probed further. Yes, there was another puncture wound, he reported, about one-half an inch to the right of the coronary artery. Had the knife moved a fraction of an inch, Cornish would have bled to death before he reached the hospital. Also—Dr. Dan paused—the left mammary artery was damaged.

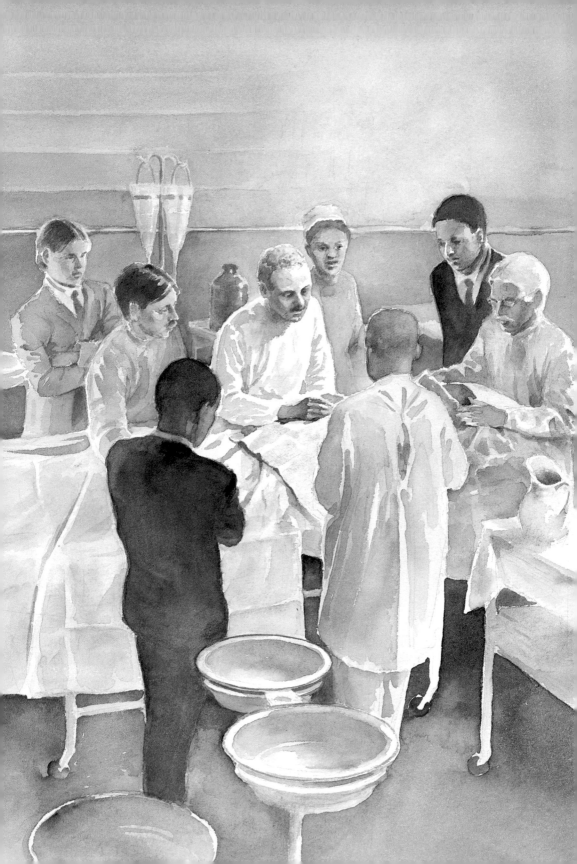

As the problems were ticked off, the atmosphere in the room grew more tense. The temperature rose above one hundred degrees. Yet not one doctor reached to wipe the perspiration that poured down hands and faces. No one took note of the time. It seemed as though the moment were somehow suspended in history, awaiting results.

Dr. Dan kept on talking and working. The small wound in the heart itself should be left undisturbed, he advised. It was slight. The tear in the pericardium was a different matter. That had to be repaired.

Now the surgeon's hands moved with a rhythm born of knowledge, practice, and instinct. Strong hands; flexible enough to pluck tunes from guitars and violins. Sure hands; steady enough to string high telephone wires. Quick hands; made nimble from years of cutting hair and trimming beards and mustaches.

These hands now raced against time to save a life. Dr. Dan tied off the injured mammary artery to prevent bleeding.

Forceps!

Now he had to try to sew up the heart's protective covering. Meticulously, he irrigated the pericardial wound with a salt solution of one hundred degrees Fahrenheit. There must be no chance of infection after the chest was closed.

Using the smooth forceps, he held together the ragged edges of the wound. Against his fingers the fist-sized heart fluttered and thumped like a frightened bird fighting to fly free.

Sutures!

Despite the rapid heartbeats, the master surgeon managed to sew up the torn edges of the pericardium. For this he used a thin catgut. After that he closed the opening he had made, again using fine catgut.

Another kind of suture would be used for the skin and cartilages, he informed the circle of watchers. He changed to silkworm gut, using long continuous sutures. This allowed for quick entry if infection or hemorrhage developed later. Over the outer sutures he applied a dry dressing.

The operation was over. James Cornish was still alive.

Dr. Dan straightened his aching back. Only then did he stop to wipe the perspiration from his face.

Like figures in a fairy tale suddenly brought to life by magic, the circle of doctors began to move and talk. They rushed to congratulate the surgeon. "Never," said one,

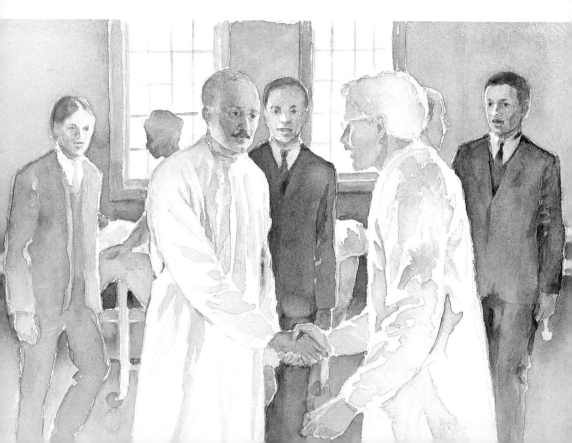

"have I seen a surgeon work so swiftly, or with so much confidence."

Each of them dashed from Provident to spread the news. Daniel Hale Williams had opened a man's chest, repaired the pericardium, closed the chest; and the patient's heart was still beating.

How long would Cornish live? Worried watchers waited in suspense. Had the doctor repaired the heart but killed the patient?

During the hours that followed the operation, Dr. Dan scarcely left Cornish's side. Alarming symptoms developed, and he made careful notes. The patient's body temperature rose to 103 degrees. His pulse raced at 134 beats a minute. Heart sounds became muffled and distant. Seizures of coughing shook his frame.

Dr. Dan shared his fears with Dr. Barr. Fluid had collected in the pleural cavity. This meant another operation.

He waited a few more days to give Cornish more time to gain strength. Three weeks after the first operation, Cornish was again rolled into the operating room. As before, Dr. Dan made an incision, this time between the seventh and eighth ribs. Through this opening he drew five pints of bloody serum.

Thanks to his careful adherence to antiseptic surgical techniques, there was no infection, and there were no further serious complications. Fifty-one days after James Cornish entered Provident with little chance of living, he was dismissed—a well man.

A news reporter from Chicago's *Inter Ocean* newspaper came to Provident to interview the surgeon and get the story first-hand. He found Dr. Dan more anxious to talk about his interracial hospital and the program for training nurses than to talk about the historic operation. The reporter had to coax details from him.

Nevertheless, the reporter's story came out with an eye-catching headline: "SEWED UP HIS HEART!" Another heading read: "DR. WILLIAMS PERFORMS AN ASTONISHING FEAT...."

The *Medical Record* of New York later carried Dr. Dan's own scientific account of the techniques and procedures he had used during the operation. His case created world-wide attention, for it was the first recorded attempt to suture the pericardium of the human heart.

His pioneering operation gave courage to other doctors to challenge death when faced with chest wounds. Dr. Dan's techniques were copied by other surgeons, step by step.

The phrase "Sewed Up His Heart" became closely associated with the name of Daniel Hale Williams. The historic operation on James Cornish helped to advance the progress toward modern heart surgery.

MEET LILLIE PATTERSON, AUTHOR

Lillie Patterson wrote the biography of Daniel Hale Williams because she thought he was someone children should know better. On writing biographies, Patterson states: "I enjoy research and will make my research as exhaustive for a simple text of less than 10,000 words as I would have done for a multi-volume work on a biographical subject. From this mass of information, I try to capture something of the spirit of the individual so that young readers will take inspiration from the life and will be led to more mature works."

BIBLIOGRAPHY

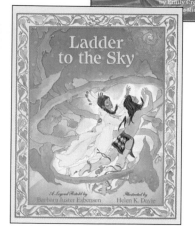

Dr. Beaumont and the Man With the Hole in His Stomach by Sam and Beryl Epstein. An unusual patient helps a doctor learn about digestion.

Germs Make Me Sick! by Melvin Berger. Read about germs, bacteria, and viruses, and the trouble they can cause.

Healing Warrior: A Story about Sister Elizabeth Kenny by Emily Crofford. A successful method of treating and rehabilitating polio patients is developed by an Australian nurse.

Ladder to the Sky by Barbara Juster Esbensen. How did the Native Americans heal their sick? This fascinating legend explains how the Ojibway Indians learned to use plants and herbs to cure the ill.

Medicine: Yesterday, Today, and Tomorrow by Dennis Brindell Fradin. The incredible story of medicine—yesterday, today, and tomorrow—is explained.

The Usborne Young Scientist: Medicine by Pam Beasant. Do you know how to treat an illness or injury? Have you ever wondered what happens during surgery? Read and discover the fascinating facts!

Path of the Pale Horse by Paul Fleischman. Lep, training to be a doctor, faces the challenges of a yellow fever epidemic in 1793 Philadelphia.

Sadako and the Thousand Paper Cranes by Eleanor Coerr. An old Japanese poem, telling of making a thousand paper cranes to live forever, gives hope to a young girl battling leukemia. Can she make enough paper cranes in time to save her life?

GLOSSARY

a as in at   o as in ox   ou as in out   ch as in chair

ā as in late   ō as in rose   u as in up   hw as in which

â as in care   ô as in bought   ûr as in turn;   ng as in ring

ä as in father   and raw   germ, learn,   sh as in shop

e as in set   oi as in coin   firm, work   th as in thin

ē as in me   o͝o as in book   ə as in about,   t͟h as in there

i as in it   o͞o as in too   chicken, pencil,   zh as in treasure

ī as in kite   or as in form   cannon, circus

The mark (´) is placed after a syllable with a heavy accent,
as in **chicken** (chik´ ən).

The mark (´) after a syllable shows a lighter accent,
as in **disappear** (dis´ ə pēr´).

abolitionist (ab´ ə lish´ ən ist) *n.* A person who wants to end slavery.

abreast (ə brest´) *adv.* Alongside of; next to.

access (ak´ ses) *n.* A chance to approach someone.

account (ə kount´) *n.* A customer or client.

accountant (ə koun´ tnt) *n.* A person whose job is to keep track of how money is earned and spent in a company.

acoustic (ə ko͞o´ stik) *adj.* Designed to control sound, especially to keep it quiet.

adapt (ə dapt´) *v.* To adjust in order to make suitable for new conditions.

adjourn (ə jûrn´) *v.* To move a meeting to another place.

advent (ad´ vent) *n.* A coming; an arrival.

aerial (âr´ ē əl) *adj.* In the air.

allotment (ə lot´ mənt) *n.* A share or part of something.

altimeter (al tim´ i tər) *n.* A device that tells how high an airplane is.

altitude (al´ ti to͞od´) *n.* The height; the distance above sea level.

amputation (am´ pyŏŏ tā´ shən) *n.*
The act of cutting off a body part
such as an arm or a leg.

anatomy (ə nat´ ə mē) *n.* The
structure of the human body.

ancestor (an´ ses tər) *n.* A
forefather; a parent, grandparent,
great-grandparent, and so on.

anesthesia (an´ əs thē´ zhə) *n.* A
loss of feeling brought about by
drugs so that surgery can be
performed.

antibiotic (an´ ti bī ot´ ik) *n.* A
chemical that kills disease germs.

antiseptic (an´ tə sep´ tik) *adj.* Free
from germs; germ-killing.

appointment (ə point´ mənt) *n.* A
job or office.

artificial (är´ tə fish´ əl) *adj.* Made
by humans rather than produced
by nature.

asepsis (ə sep´ sis) *n.* The methods
used to make sure there are no
germs.

assert (ə sûrt´) *v.* To say firmly.

authoritative (ə thor´ i tā´ tiv) *adj.*
Bossy; masterful.

aviation (ā´ vē ā´ shən) *n.* The art
or science of flying aircraft.

bacteria (bak ter´ e ə) *n. pl.* Disease
germs; one-celled organisms that
can be seen only with a
microscope.

bank (bangk) *v.* To tilt an aircraft
to one side while flying it.

bankruptcy (bangk´ rupt sē) *n.*
The condition of being legally
declared unable to pay one's
debts.

beguile (bi gīl´) *v.* To tempt; to
charm; to amuse.

bid (bid) *v.* To offer a price for
something.

blood pressure (blud´ presh´ ər) *n.*
The amount of force with which
blood presses against the insides of
the body's blood vessels.

bookkeeping (bŏŏk´ kē´ ping) *n.*
Keeping a record of money earned
and spent in a company.

brandish (bran´ dish) *v.* To shake;
to wave.

bushel (bŏŏsh´ əl) *n.* A
measurement consisting of
8 gallons, or 32 quarts.

capacity (kə pas´ i tē) *n.* The
ability.

caress (kə res´) *v.* To stroke softly.

cartilage (kär´ tl ij) *n.* Firm yet flexible tissue that is inside the human body.

casket (kas´ kit) *n.* A small box or chest.

catgut (kat´ gut´) *n.* A strong thread made of dried animals' intestines, used in surgery to make stitches.

century (sen´ chə rē) *n.* 100 years.

chamber (chām´ bər) *n.* A private room.

chartreuse (shär trōōz´) *n.* A yellowish green color.

chemist (kem´ ist) *n.* A scientist who studies what substances are made of.

chock (chok) *n.* A wedge or block used to keep things from moving.

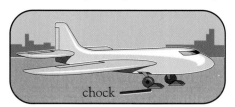

chock

colander (kul´ ən dər) *n.* A bowl with many small holes in it, used as a strainer in cooking.

colleague (kol´ ēg) *n.* A member of the same profession as another person.

complication (kom´ pli kā´ shən) *n.* Another disease that makes a person's original disease get worse.

compound (kom´ pound) *n.* A closed-in area containing homes or other buildings.

comptroller (kən trō´ lər) *n.* Controller; a chief accountant or government official.

concoction (kon kok´ shən) *n.* Something made up or invented.

condemnation (kon´ dem nā´ shən) *n.* A judgment of guilty.

condominium (kon´ də min´ ē əm) *n.* An apartment that a person owns instead of rents.

confidence (kon´ fi dəns) *n.* A belief in one's own ability.

confirm (kən fûrm´) *v.* To make sure.

consent (kən sent´) *v.* To agree.

console (kən sōl´) *v.* To comfort.

consternation (kon´ stər nā´ shən) *n.* Dismay; dread; anxiety.

consult (kən sult´) *v.* To ask advice.

consumer (kən sōō´ mər) *n.* A person who buys and uses products.

consumptive (kən sump´ tiv) *adj.* Sick with the disease tuberculosis, a lung infection.

contaminated (kən tam´ ə nā´ təd) *adj.* Unclean; mixed with something dirty.

contract (kon´ trakt) *n.* A formal, written agreement.

cope (kōp) *v.* To handle successfully.

coronary artery (kor´ ə ner ē är´ tə rē) *n.* An artery in the heart that supplies blood to the parts of the heart.

crude (krōōd) *adj.* Rough; simple.

cuffing (kuf´ ing) *n.* A series of slaps.

curandera (kōō´ rän de´ rä) *n.* A woman healer who uses folk medicine such as herbs and other plants to cure illness.

currycomb (kûr´ ē kōm´) *v.* To rub down a horse with a special comb.

debt (det) *n.* Anything one owes.

deed (dēd) *n.* An action; a thing done.

depression (di presh´ ən) *n.* A period of time when many businesses and people do not have enough money.

desolately (des´ ə lit lē) *adv.* In a hopeless or lonely way.

desperately (des´ pər it lē) *adv.* Hopelessly.

destine (des´ tin) *v.* To set aside for a particular purpose.

devise (di vīz´) *v.* To figure out; to make up.

diabetic (dī´ ə bet´ ik) *adj.* Having the disease diabetes, in which a person's body cannot properly process sugar or starch.

diagnosis (dī´ əg nō´ sis) *n.* The identification of a person's disease.

dietician (dī´ i tish´ ən) *n.* A person who is an expert in food and nutrition.

digestive system (di jes´ tiv sis´ təm) *n.* The stomach, intestines, and other organs that process food in the body.

disadvantage (dis´ əd van´ tij) *n.* A drawback; something that makes an action more difficult.

discount (dis´ kount) *n.* A sum taken away from a bill.

disinfect (dis´ in fekt´) *v.* To cleanse of infection; to make free of germs.

dismayed (dis mād´) *adj.* Discouraged; alarmed.

dispel (di spel´) *v.* To drive away; to banish.

distinguishing (di sting´ gwish ing) *n.* Making noticeable; making a difference.

don (don) *v.* To put on.

douse (dous) *v.* To splash.

dressing (dres´ ing) *n.* The cloth or other material used to cover a wound.

dubiously (dōō´ bē əs lē) *adv.* Doubtfully; in an unsure way.

economic (ek´ ə nom´ ik) *adj.* Having to do with money.

eloquence (el´ ə kwəns) *n.* The ability to express ideas clearly.

embark (em bärk´) *v.* To begin a journey.

eminent (em´ ə nənt) *adj.* Celebrated; well-known; grand.

emulate (em´ yə lāt´) *v.* To imitate.

en route (än rōōt´) *adv.* Along the way.

enchain (en chān´) *v.* To tie down or hold back.

encounter (en koun´ tər) *v.* To meet by chance.

engulf (en gulf´) *v.* To swallow up; to overcome.

enterprise (en´ tər prīz´) *n.* A business or company.

enviously (en´ vē əs lē) *adv.* With jealousy.

epidemic (ep´ i dem´ ik) *n.* An outbreak of disease that spreads quickly to many people.

erratic (i rat´ ik) *adj.* Changeable; not reliable.

escort (i skort´) *v.* To go with and protect.

estimate (es´ tə māt´) *v.* To figure out the cost of something in advance. —*n.* (es´ tə mit) A statement given in advance telling what a service will cost.

exasperated (ig zas´ pə rā´ təd) *adj.* Irritated; angry.

executive (ig zek´ yə tiv) *n.* A person who has the right or power to make decisions and run a company.

expectancy (ik spek´ tən sē) *n.* A state of waiting for something to happen. **life expectancy:** The number of years the average person will live.

expertise (ek´ spər tēz´) *n.* Special skill or knowledge.

external (ik stûr´ nl) *adj.* Outside; outward.

facilities (fə sil´ i tēz) *n. pl.* Things designed to make a task easier or more convenient.

fatal (fāt´ l) *adj.* Deadly; causing death.

feisty (fī´ stē) *adj.* Full of energy.

ferry (fer´ ē) *v.* To carry across a river or a bay. —*n.* A boat that carries passengers, vehicles, or goods across a river or a bay; a ferryboat.

fibrous (fī´ brəs) *adj.* Containing fibers, or long, narrow strips or cords.

finance (fi nans´) *n.* Money matters or dealings.

flank (flangk) *n.* The side.

fleece (flēs) *n.* A sheep's coat of wool.

folly (fol´ ē) *n.* Foolishness.

forceps (for´ səps) *n.* Small pliers used in surgery.

forlorn (for lorn´) *adj.* Sad and lonely; friendless.

format (for´ mat) *n.* The way something is laid out or organized.

fowl (foul) *n.* A bird such as a chicken or a turkey.

galleon (gal´ ē ən) *n.* A type of large sailing ship used in the 1400s through the 1600s.

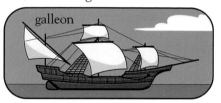
galleon

game (gām) *n.* Wild animals that are hunted.

game reserve (gām´ ri zûrv´) *n.* An area of land set aside for wild animals to live in without being hunted.

garret (gar´ it) *n.* An attic.

gauge (gāj) *n.* A device that measures something.

generation (jen´ ə rā´ shən) *n.* A group of people who are all about the same age.

genteel (jen tēl´) *adj.* Well-bred; polite.

gesture (jes´ chər) *n.* A body movement that shows meaning.

ghetto (get´ ō) *n.* A part of any city that is largely inhabited by members of a particular racial, ethnic, or minority group.

glib (glib) *adj.* Smooth-talking; persuasive.

gorge (gorj) *n.* A steep, narrow opening between mountains; a small canyon.

gossamer (gos´ ə mər) *adj.* Light; thin; flimsy.

gout (gout) *n.* A painful swelling of the joints and the toes.

grater (grā´ tər) *n.* A kitchen tool that one uses to grind food into small pieces by rubbing the food against its sharp, rough metal edges.

grippe (grip) *n.* Influenza; the flu.

gyrocompass (jī´ rō kum´ pəs) *n.* A device that tells what direction one is going.

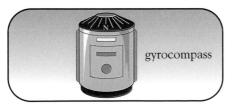
gyrocompass

half-pence (hā´ pəns) *n.* A British coin worth half a penny, not made after 1984.

harness (här´ nis) *v.* To put leather straps on an animal for a particular purpose.

haughty (hô´ tē) *adj.* Full of pride.

haunting (hôn´ ting) *adj.* Staying in the mind; not forgotten quickly.

havoc (hav´ ək) *n.* Destruction; ruin.

headwind (hed´ wind´) *n.* A wind that is blowing opposite the way an object such as an airplane is traveling.

hearthstone (härth´ stōn´) *n.* The stone floor of a fireplace.

hemorrhage (hem´ ər ij) *n.* Heavy bleeding.

hose (hōz) *n.* Stockings.

hullabaloo (hul´ ə bə loͦo´) *n.* An uproar; a lot of noise.

hygiene (hī´ jēn) *n.* Keeping oneself clean in order to stay healthy.

identity (ī den´ ti tē) *n.* The condition that makes something special.

immaculate (i mak´ yə lit) *adj.* Extremely clean; spotless.

immune (i myōōn´) *adj.* Free from; not able to get a certain disease.

impact (im´ pakt) *n.* An influence or an effect.

impair (im pâr´) *v.* To weaken; to injure.

impracticable (im prak´ ti kə bəl) *adj.* Not possible with the methods or equipment available.

impurity (im pyŏŏr´ i tē) *n.* Something that is mixed with other things or is not pure.

incision (in sizh´ ən) *n.* A cut made into the body during surgery.

income (in´ kum) *n.* The total money received.

incorporated (in kor´ pə rā´ tid) *adj.* Legally made into a corporation, which is a type of business in which the company itself is separate from the people who own it.

indignantly (in dig´ nənt lē) *adv.* With anger; with an insulted feeling.

ineffectively (in´ i fek´ tiv lē) *adv.* Uselessly; in vain.

inevitable (in ev´ i tə bəl) *adj.* Bound to happen; impossible to avoid.

inexperienced (in´ ik spēr´ ē ənst) *adj.* Lacking training or practice.

infirm (in fûrm´) *adj.* Weak; sickly.

infirmary (in fûr´ mə rē) *n.* A place where sick people are treated.

inflated (in flā´ tid) *adj.* Made larger.

initial (i nish´ əl) *adj.* First.

insulin (in´ sə lin) *n.* A commercially prepared substance used for treating diabetes. The pancreas produces insulin in a person without diabetes.

intense (in tens´) *adj.* Strong; deep.

interest (in´ tər ist) *n.* Money received on an investment.

intern (in´ tûrn) *n.* A doctor who is being trained at a hospital.

internal (in tûr´ nl) *adj.* Inside; inner.

interracial (in´ tər rā´ shəl) *adj.* Including people of different races.

intimidate (in tim´ i dāt´) *v.* To threaten; to frighten.

intrigue (in trēg´) *v.* To fascinate; to interest.

inundate (in´ ən dāt´) *v.* To swamp; to flood; to overwhelm.

invest (in vest´) *v.* To spend money on a company, hoping to receive profits.

investment (in vest´ mənt) *n.* The use of money to gain profit.

irrigate (ir´ i gāt) v. To wash with water or other liquid.

kindling (kind´ ling) n. Small pieces of wood or scraps used for starting a fire.

labor (lā´ bər) n. The beginning of the process of birth.

lading (lā´ ding) n. A shipment; a cargo; a load. **bill of lading:** A receipt listing the items in a shipment and their value.

landfall (land´ fôl´) n. A sighting of land.

lapse (laps) v. To fall; to sink.

learned (lûr´ nid) adj. Having knowledge; educated.

liaison (lē ā´ zən) n. A person whose job is to be sure that all parts of an organization cooperate with each other.

lofty (lôf´ tē) adj. 1. Noble; grand. 2. High; tall.

log (lôg) v. To travel a certain distance —n. An official journal or diary.

lull (lul) v. To put to sleep by soothing.

mandolin (man´ dl in) n. A stringed musical instrument.

mandolin

maneuver (mə noo´ vər) v. To move in a planned way.

manifold ring (man´ ə fōld´ ring´) n. An engine part that gas or fluid flows through.

manipulate (mə nip´ yə lāt´) v. To handle or control.

market (mär´ kit) n. The people who are likely to buy a certain product.

marketing (mär´ ki ting) n. All the activities that lead to selling a product, including advertising, packaging, and selling.

media (mē´ dē ə) n. Avenues of communication to the public, such as newspapers and television.

menacing (men´ is ing) adj. Dangerous; threatening.

mesa (mā´ sə) n. High, flat land, like a plateau but smaller.

metalsmith (met´ l smith´) *n.* A person who makes things out of metal.

meteorologist (mē´ tē ə rol´ ə jist) *n.* A person who studies the earth's atmosphere and weather.

meticulously (mə tik´ yə ləs lē) *adv.* In an extremely careful and precise way.

microbe (mī´ krōb) *n.* An organism that is too small to be seen without a microscope.

mill (mil) *n.* A factory.

mock (mok) *adj.* Pretended.

monies (mun´ ēz) *n. pl.* Funds; a plural of *money.*

morale (mə ral´) *n.* Mental condition; the courage and spirit to do one's duty.

mortal (mor´ tl) *n.* A human being.

muslin (muz´ lin) *n.* A kind of cotton cloth.

muster (mus´ tər) *v.* To gather.

mystified (mis´ tə fīd´) *adj.* Bewildered; confused.

NAACP National Association for the Advancement of Colored People.

native (nā´ tiv) *adj.* Belonging to by birth.

niche (nich) *n.* One's place in society.

novel (nov´ əl) *adj.* New.

obsession (əb sesh´ ən) *n.* Something that a person thinks about all the time.

odds (odz) *n.* The chances that something will or will not happen.

ominous (om´ ə nəs) *adj.* Unfavorable; threatening misfortune.

oriented (or´ ē en´ tid) *adj.* Geared or directed toward.

outstanding (out´ stan´ ding) *adj.* Remaining unpaid.

pachyderm (pak´ i dûrm´) *n.* Any large, thick-skinned, hoofed animal, such as the elephant.

pantheon (pan´ thē on´) *n.* A group made up of all the heroes of a certain type.

pitch (pich) *v.* To lurch or fall suddenly.

plague (plāg) *n.* Any widespread disease; a disease that is spread in an epidemic.

plummet (plum´ it) *v.* To plunge; to drop.

pneumonia (nŏŏ mōn´ yə) *n.* A disease of the lungs.

poacher (pō´ chər) *n.* A person who catches animals in a place where hunting is against the law.

policy (pol´ ə sē) *n.* A method of action and procedure.

ponder (pon´ dər) *v.* To think about.

poppet (pop´ it) *n. British. dialect.* A nickname showing affection, meaning "child."

port (port) *n.* A place or town where ships come to load or unload.

poultice (pōl´ tis) *n.* A wad of something soft and moist, placed over a wound to heal it.

precision (pri sizh´ ən) *n.* Exactness; accuracy with details.

procession (prə sesh´ ən) *n.* A line of people moving forward in an orderly and ceremonial manner.

profit (prof´ it) *n.* The earnings gained from a business.

profusely (prə fyōōs´ lē) *adv.* In abundance; in large amounts.

promote (prə mōt´) *v.* To encourage people to buy something by advertising it.

prophet (prof´ it) *n.* One who tells things that will happen in the future.

prospect (pros´ pekt) *n.* A future possible event; something that could happen.

prostration (pros trā´ shən) *n.* Exhaustion; extreme tiredness.

P.S. Public School.

pulse (puls) *n.* The regular beating of the heart.

puree (pyōō rā´) *v.* To make a solid food into a thick liquid.

ram (ram) *n.* A male sheep.

rash (rash) *adj.* Hasty; reckless.

reception (ri sep´ shən) *n.* A party held to welcome someone.

refurbish (rē fûr´ bish) *v.* To renew; to renovate.

reluctantly (ri luk´ tənt lē) *adv.* Not willingly.

resentment (ri zent´ mənt) *n.* A feeling of being insulted.

reservation (rez´ ər vā´ shən) *n.* The land set aside for Native Americans to live on.

resolve (ri zolv´) *v.* To make a decision.

retire (ri tīr´) *v.* To go away to a private place.

revitalize (rē vīt´ l īz´) *v.* To bring new life to.

sac (sak) *n.* An inner body structure that is like a bag.

scalding (skôl ding) *n.* An injury caused by hot liquid or steam.

scalpel (skal´ pəl) *n.* A small, straight, light knife used by surgeons.

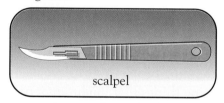
scalpel

serum (sēr´ əm) *n.* The liquid part of blood.

shan't (shant) Contraction of **shall not:** Will not.

sheepish (shē´ pish) *adj.* Timid; bashful; shy.

shock (shok) *n.* 1. A thick, bushy mass. 2. A dangerous condition in which a person's blood circulation becomes extremely slow.

shrewd (shrood) *adj.* Clever; wise.

siege (sēj) *n.* A group of illnesses, one after the other.

silkworm gut (silk´ wûrm gut´) *n.* Silk thread used in surgery.

site (sīt) *n.* The ground occupied by a building.

slew (sloo) *v.* Past tense of **slay:** To kill violently.

snare (snâr) *n.* A trap.

solder (sod´ ər) *v.* To join metal pieces together by using a liquid metal at a joint.

solo (sō´ lō) *adv.* Alone; on one's own. —*v.* To fly an airplane by oneself.

solution (sə loo´ shən) *n.* A liquid that has something dissolved in it.

sough (sou) *v.* To make a sound like rushing, rustling, or murmuring.

sow (sō) *v.* To plant; to scatter seeds.

span (span) *n.* The part of a bridge between its two ends.

speculation (spek´ yə lā´ shən) *n.* Thought; wondering.

spit (spit) *n.* A rod on which meat is roasted over a fire.

status (stā´ təs) *n.* Condition; situation.

steadfast (sted´ fast´) *adj.* Firm; unmoving.

sterilize (ster´ ə līz´) *v.* To make free from germs.

Pronunciation Key: at; lāte; câre; fäther; set; mē; it; kīte; ox; rōse; ô in bought; coin; bŏŏk; tōō; form; out; up; tûrn; ə sound in about, chicken, pencil, cannon, circus; chair; **hw** in **wh**ich; ring; **sh**op; **th**in; **th**ere; **zh** in trea**s**ure.

sternum (stûr´nəm) *n.* The breastbone; the flat, narrow, bony area to which the ribs are attached.

stethoscope (steth´ə skōp´) *n.* An instrument for listening to sounds within the body.

stock (stok) *v.* To keep a supply of a product ready for sale. —*n.* 1. All of the animals on a farm; livestock. 2. A share or part ownership in a company or corporation.

stout (stout) *adj.* Strongly made; sturdy.

strain (strān) *v.* 1. To make something pass through a filter or object with small holes in order to remove water or larger pieces. 2. To overwork; to work to the utmost.

stylus (stī´ləs) *n.* A pointed writing instrument.

subcontracting (sub kon´trakt ing) *n.* Hiring other companies to do one's job.

submit (səb mit´) *v.* To give something for consideration.

summon (sum´ən) *v.* To send for; to call someone to come.

superstition (sōō´pər stish´ən) *n.* A belief in magic; a belief that is not based on reason.

supportive (sə por´tiv) *adj.* Encouraging; helpful.

suture (sōō´chər) *v.* To stitch together; to sew up.

symptom (simp´təm) *n.* A sign that indicates what kind of illness someone has.

tactful (takt´fəl) *adj.* Skilled at speaking and acting without offending people; able to avoid saying things that might upset or insult someone.

tally (tal´ē) *v.* To count or add up.

taut (tôt) *adj.* Stretched tight; tense.

tedious (tē´dē əs) *adj.* Wearisome; tiring; boring.

thatched (thacht) *adj.* Covered with straw.

thatched

thrash (thrash) *v.* To beat.

threshold (thresh´ ōld) *n.* The bottom part of a doorway; the sill.

throes (thrōz) *n.* Any violent spasm or struggle.

toll (tōl) *n.* Damage; destruction.

tottery (tot´ ə rē) *adj.* Unsteady; shaky.

tout (tout) *v.* To describe in a boastful way; to overpraise.

transcontinental (trans´ kon tn en´ tl) *adj.* Extending across a continent.

transfusion (trans fyōō´ zhən) *n.* A transfer of blood into a person.

trespassing (tres´ pəs ing) *n.* Going onto another's property without permission.

turban (tûr´ bən) *n.* A headdress for a man, made by wrapping a long strip of cloth around the head.

turbulence (tûr´ byə ləns) *n.* Violent weather conditions.

ultimatum (ul´ tə mā´ təm) *n.* A last or final demand or proposal.

uncharted (un chär´ tid) *adj.* Not shown on a map; not explored; not known.

unique (yōō nēk´) *adj.* Having no equal; one of a kind.

unpredictable (un´ pri dik´ tə bəl) *adj.* Not certain; changeable.

usher (ush´ ər) *v.* To escort or take someone someplace.

vaccine (vak sēn´) *n.* A preparation, usually liquid, given to prevent a disease.

vagabond (vag´ ə bond´) *adj.* Wandering aimlessly from place to place.

verbal (vûr´ bəl) *adj.* Spoken, not written.

verge (vûrj) *n.* The place where something begins; the brink.

vermin (vûr´ min) *n.* Small creatures that damage food or property.

vertical (vûr´ ti kəl) *adj.* Upright; from top to bottom.

vital (vīt´ l) *adj.* Necessary for life.

vouch (vouch) *v.* To bear witness; to confirm.

warden (wor´ dn) *n.* An officer in charge; a supervisor.

whitecap (hwīt´ kap´) *n.* The broken, foamy tip of a wave in rough weather.

wrath (rath) *n.* Anger; rage.

continued from page 5

Gloria D. Miklowitz and Madeleine Yates: An excerpt entitled "Gregg Nevarez, Young Tycoon" from *The Young Tycoons* by Gloria D. Miklowitz and Madeleine Yates, copyright © 1981 by Gloria D. Miklowitz and Madeleine Yates.

New York City Commission on the Status of Women: "Dorothy Brunson: The Making of an Entrepreneur" by Jacqueline Paris-Chitanvis from *Women Making History: Conversations with Fifteen New Yorkers*, edited by Maxine Gold, copyright © 1985 by New York City Commission on the Status of Women.

G. P. Putnam's Sons: "The Acrobats" by Dorothy Aldis from *Hop, Skip and Jump!* by Dorothy Aldis, copyright 1934, © 1961 by Dorothy Aldis.

Scholastic Inc., New York: "Ice Cream Cones: A New Scoop" from *What If: Fifty Discoveries That Changed the World* by Dian Dincin Buchman and Seli Groves, copyright © 1977 by Dian Dincin Buchman and Seli Groves.

Charles Scribner's Sons, an imprint of Macmillan Publishing Co.: *Dick Whittington and His Cat* by Marcia Brown, copyright 1950 by Marcia Brown, copyright © renewed 1977 by Marcia Brown.

Troll Associates: *Jason and the Golden Fleece* by C. J. Naden, illustrated by Robert Baxter, copyright © 1981 by Troll Associates.

Wieser & Wieser, Inc., New York: An excerpt entitled "The New Doctor" from *You Can Hear a Magpie Smile* by Paula G. Paul, copyright © 1980 by Paula G. Paul.

Photography
43 Anne MacLachlan
111 Bill Burkhart
    Sean Kernan
129 Katherine Lambert Photography
167 UPI/Bettmann
214 National Library of Medicine
    New York Downtown Hospital
    The Wellcome Center for Medical Science
    The Bettmann Archive
    Historical Pictures/Stock Montage
    World Health Organization
215 National Library of Medicine
    Giraudon/Art Resource
    The Bettmann Archive
    Historical Pictures/Stock Montage
    World Health Organization
227 Romana Prokopiw

COLOPHON

This book has been designed in the classic style to emphasize our commitment to classic literature. The typeface, Goudy Old Style, was drawn in 1915 by Frederic W. Goudy, who based it on fifteenth-century Italian letterforms.

The art has been drawn to reflect the golden age of children's book illustration and its recent rebirth in the work of innovative artists of today. This book was designed by John Grandits. Composition, electronic page makeup, and photo and art management were provided by The Chestnut House Group, Inc.